THE SCHOLARSHIP SERIES IN BIOLOGY

General Editor: W. H. Dowdeswell

STUDIES IN INVERTEBRATE BEHAVIOUR

THE SCHOLARSHIP SERIES IN BIOLOGY

General Editor—W. H. Dowdeswell

Human Blood Groups and Inheritance
by S. Lawler and L. J. Lawler

Woodland Ecology
by E. G. Neal

New Concepts in Flowering Plant Taxonomy
by J. Heslop Harrison

The Mechanism of Evolution
by W. H. Dowdeswell

Some Aspects of Life in Fresh Water
by E. J. Popham

Heathland Ecology
by C. P. Friedlander

The Organization of the Central Nervous System
by C. V. Brewer

Plant Metabolism
by G. A. Strafford

Comparative Physiology of Vertebrate Respiration
by G. M. Hughes

Animal Body Fluids and their Regulation
by A. P. M. Lockwood

Life on the Sea-shore
by A. J. Southward

Chalkland Ecology
by John Sankey

Ecology of Parasites
by N. A. Croll

Physiological Aspects of Water and Plant Life
by W. M. M. Baron

Biological Principles in Fermentation
by J. G. Carr

Studies in Invertebrate Behaviour
by S. M. Evans

STUDIES IN INVERTEBRATE BEHAVIOUR

by

S. M. EVANS, B.Sc., Ph.D.

Senior Biology Master
Archbishop Holgate's Grammar
School, York

HEINEMANN EDUCATIONAL
BOOKS LTD : LONDON

Heinemann Educational Books Ltd
LONDON MELBOURNE TORONTO
JOHANNESBURG SINGAPORE AUCKLAND
IBADAN HONG KONG NAIROBI

First published 1968

Published by
Heinemann Educational Books Ltd
48 Charles Street, London W.1
Printed in Great Britain by
Richard Clay (The Chaucer Press) Ltd,
Bungay, Suffolk

Contents

Preface

The almost incredible range of invertebrate behaviour is often a source of interest and fascination to the sixth-form and undergraduate biologist. Unfortunately there are few books available for him to increase his knowledge of this subject, particularly at an introductory level, and, in writing this one, I hope that I shall have helped to fill this gap in the literature.

Naturally it is necessary to be selective in such a short book. However, in choosing material I have given preference to research that, in my opinion, makes an important contribution to our understanding of either the function or the mechanisms of animal behaviour. In fact, a point that is not always fully appreciated is that invertebrates may have a valuable role to play in studies of this kind. Compared with vertebrates, whose nervous systems and behaviour are alarmingly complicated and, perhaps, too complex for us to understand at present, invertebrates have relatively simple nervous systems and behavioural repertoires. Furthermore, their nervous systems are usually more accessible and more amenable to investigation than those of vertebrates.

I hope that the reader will be sufficiently interested to refer to the reading list at the end of the book. This includes works of general interest as well as reviews and papers describing original research. They have been selected to cover most of the topics covered in the book and should provide the reader with an opportunity of reading more fully into fields that attract him.

My thanks are due to Dr. Margaret Bastock for her valuable criticisms of the manuscript and to Professor R. B. Clark and Mr. W. H. Dowdeswell for criticisms of parts of it. I should also like to thank Mr. Hamish MacGibbon for his help with various publishing problems that have arisen, and my wife for her patience during the preparation of the book.

STEWART EVANS
York, 1968

1
Introduction

The behaviour of an animal must be as effective an adaptation to its environment as its structure if it is to survive in the struggle for existence. It must be able to find shelter, to recognise mates, food and predators and react appropriately to them whenever they are encountered. Basically there are two ways in which behaviour becomes adapted to these needs. The animal may be endowed with an inherited repertoire of responses, which are performed effectively as soon as the situation demands, without the need for practice or previous experience. Simple reflex responses certainly come into this category, but so do the more elaborate patterns of behaviour, such as web-building and prey-capture in spiders, which are called instinctive. Alternatively, the animal may acquire new responses during its life as a result of its individual experience that is to say, it learns how to react in certain situations.

However, there is no absolute distinction between instinct and learning. Behaviour often fails to fall exactly into either of these categories because it contains elements of both of them. For example, bumblebees are initially attracted to flowers by instinctive responses to their sight and scent, but these responses sometimes become modified by learning. It has been shown by studying individuals marked with dabs of coloured paint, that they often spend several days foraging from one particular kind of plant and, in doing so, learn to recognise it by some of its more obvious features. Regular visitors to hound's tongue, which has small inconspicuous flowers, learn to recognise the general shape of the plant and will then visit plants that have been deflowered. They even search in the leaf axils, where the flowers are normally borne, as if they had learned where to look for them. The information learned depends on the kind of plant visited. Bumblebees visiting foxgloves are never attracted to deflowered plants so that they do not apparently learn to recognise the plants by their shape. But they do become conditioned to the colour of the large, conspicuous flowers and, as a result, will visit previously unattractive, purple-coloured, paper models of flowers.

However, apart from one or two notable exceptions (see Chapter 8), most invertebrates seem to have poorly developed abilities to learn and depend almost entirely on instinctive responses. Such learning ability that many of them do possess serves only to modify the range of stimuli that will elicit otherwise instinctive patterns of behaviour. This is in marked contrast with mammals which show the extreme in learning ability and often learn whole patterns of responses. But, unlike mammals, most invertebrates do not have a long, protected juvenile development to acquire new responses. The majority of them fend for themselves from birth and need preset behaviour to do so.

Flexibility and rigidity of instinctive behaviour

Inborn patterns of behaviour are sometimes remarkably complex, particularly among arthropods, and it is in this phylum that the elaboration of instinctive behaviour seems to have reached its peak. Some of the most impressive examples are provided by solitary wasps of the family *Sphegidae*, which construct nests and stock them with food for their developing larvae. Females of one of them, the digger wasp *Ammophila campestris*, dig nests in the ground, consisting of a vertical shaft about 2½ cm deep, with an ovoid cell at the bottom. A single larva develops in the cell and this feeds on caterpillars, which are captured and paralysed by the female, dragged back to the nest by her and deposited in the cell.

Professor G. P. Baerends has shown that a female wasp may

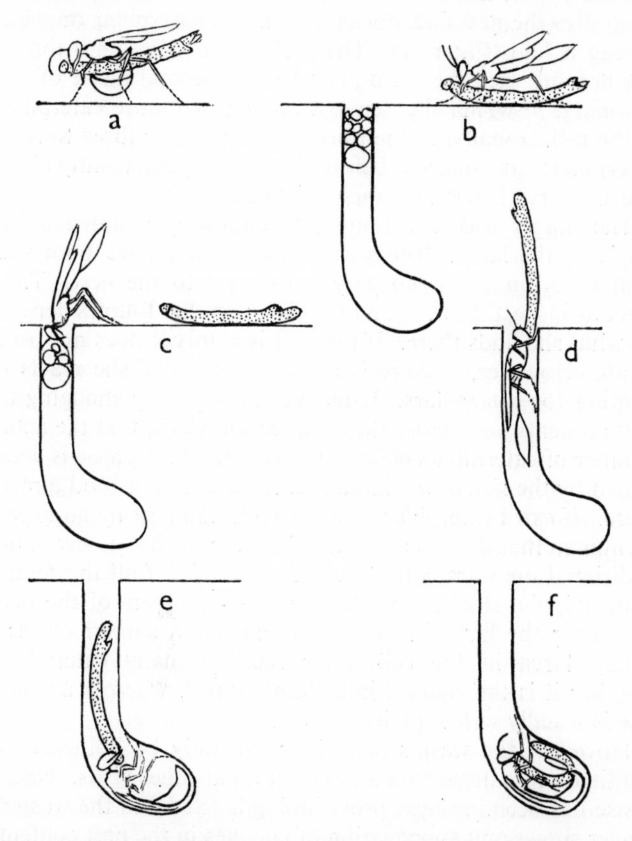

Figure 1. A female digger wasp *Ammophila campestris* in the successive acts of (*a*) stinging her prey, (*b*) transporting it to her burrow, (*c–e*) stocking it there and (*f*) laying an egg on it. (*Redrawn from Schneirla, after Baerends.*)

care for several nests simultaneously, but each of them is catered for in three separate phases. In the first phase, the wasp digs the nest and stocks it with one caterpillar on which an egg is laid (Figure 1). The nest is left alone until the egg hatches and then the wasp performs the second phase of provisioning, in which she deposits one or two more caterpillars in the cell. Finally, in the third phase, another three to seven caterpillars are collected before the nest is permanently closed and the larva is left to complete its development.

The digger wasp's actions are beautifully adapted to the needs of the larva. The second and third phases both start with visits on which no prey is brought to the nest. These serve as inspection visits and provisioning that follows depends on what she finds there. If the nest is empty it does not occur at all. However, if there is a larva in the cell she reacts by hunting for caterpillars. It has been shown, by changing the nest contents just before these inspection visits, that the actual number of caterpillars collected during the next phase is determined by the size of the larva and the amount of food already there. If extra caterpillars are placed in the nest by an experimenter so that there is abundant food for the larva, few, if any additional ones are collected. Alternatively, if all the food is removed, she stocks the cell with large numbers of the prey. Changing the larva in the nest often has a similar effect: a young larva in the cell never receives many caterpillars, whether it is the rightful inhabitant or not, whereas an older one is usually well supplied with them.

However, the wasp's behaviour can only be influenced at the time of an inspection and not at all at other visits. Once a phase has been initiated provisioning is fixed and the wasp no longer shows any appreciation of changes in the nest contents. Alterations in either the amount of food in the cell or the larva are ignored by her. She will even complete the third phase by permanently closing the nest entrance when the larva and all of its food have been removed just before the final visit.

Many instinctive acts that are apparently plastic and variable in normal circumstances are equally inflexible in unusual or unnatural situations. For example, the female digger wasp's action of dragging the caterpillar into the burrow is still con-

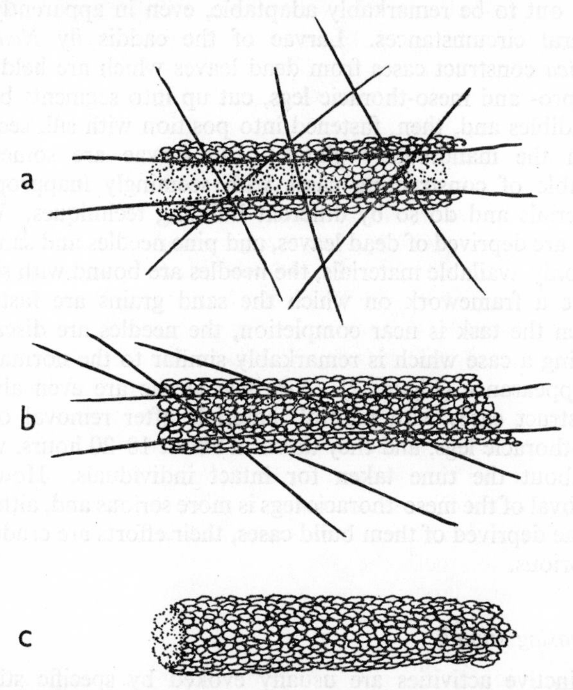

Figure 2. Three stages in the construction of the case by a caddis fly larva *Neuronia postica* using pine needles and sand as building materials. (*a*) The pine needles are used to form a framework to which sand grains are attached. (*b*) Some pine needles have been discarded and sand grains have been used to fill the gaps. (*c*) The finished case; all the needles have been removed. (*After Fankhauser and Reik.*)

tinued until she has almost disappeared into the nest, even if the caterpillar is carefully taken away from her. Similarly house-flies, *Musca*, continue to make wing-cleaning movements with the hind-legs when the wings have been amputated.

If artificial paper wings are glued on to the thorax, the cleaning movements are directed towards these.

Nevertheless some complex patterns of instinctive behaviour turn out to be remarkably adaptable, even in apparently unnatural circumstances. Larvae of the caddis fly *Neuronia postica* construct cases from dead leaves which are held with the pro- and meso-thoracic legs, cut up into segments by the mandibles and, then, fastened into position with silk secreted from the mandibulary glands. But larvae are sometimes capable of constructing cases with seemingly inappropriate materials and do so by different building techniques. When they are deprived of dead leaves, and pine needles and sand are the only available materials, the needles are bound with silk to make a framework on which the sand grains are fastened. When the task is near completion, the needles are discarded leaving a case which is remarkably similar to the normal one in appearance (Figure 2). *Neuronia* larvae are even able to construct cases with natural materials after removal of the pro-thoracic legs, and they do so in about 18–20 hours, which is about the time taken for intact individuals. However, removal of the meso-thoracic legs is more serious and, although larvae deprived of them build cases, their efforts are crude and laborious.

Releasing stimuli

Instinctive activities are usually evoked by specific stimuli, known as releasing or sign stimuli. These are usually derived from the object to which the behaviour is directed. For example, the first act in the sequence of courtship responses of the male Grayling butterfly *Eumenis semele* is released by the appearance of a female. He waits on the ground and reacts by flying upwards and pursuing her. However, it is unlikely that the male reacts to the image of the female as a whole because, as Professor N. Tinbergen and his colleagues have shown, he can be induced to follow crude models of females drawn above the ground on the end of a fine thread. Indeed, there is strong evidence that only some of her features contribute to releasing the response. Her characteristic dancing flight seems to play an important role because models pulled along in a jerky manner, to simulate this flight, are pursued more readily than models drawn smoothly along. Similarly, size is important and male Graylings are more responsive to life-size models than to larger or smaller ones. But, surprisingly, the colour and pattern of the female's wings and her general body shape seem to have little or no releasing value. Models with wings taken from real females are no more attractive than plain paper models and triangular and rectangular ones are approached as readily as those that resemble the female Grayling in outline.

Visual stimuli are also important in releasing courtship and feeding responses in the Trinidad butterfly *Heliconius* and these can also be evoked by models. Hungry butterflies react to suitable paper models of flowers by alighting on them and often probing them with the proboscis. The colour of the model is important and, although butterflies sometimes attempt to feed from models in the entire spectrum range, yellow and yellow-orange ones are visited most frequently. Colour also has a high releasing value for courtship responses, but in this case red, which has little attraction for individuals searching for flowers, is the important colour. Both the male and female *Heliconius* have a conspicuous red band across each fore-wing and it has been shown by artificially altering the colour of the wings that the more the colour varies from normal the less successful individuals become in eliciting courtship in other butterflies. All black *Heliconius* are notably unsuccessful in this respect. Similarly the only models that evoke strong courtship responses are those coloured red, violet-red or orange.

Releasing stimuli are, of course, by no means always visual. Vibrations in the web caused by struggling prey release the approach response in the house spider *Archaearanea tepidariorium.* Vibration receptors are located at the tarsal-metatarsal joints of the legs. The spiders orientate themselves with speed and accuracy towards the source of vibrations but they will only approach an object producing a frequency between 400 and 700 c/s which is in the frequency range of the wing-beat of many insects. The subsequent behaviour, when the prey is captured and killed, which has been analysed in *Epeira diademata*, is released by other stimuli. Both chemical and tactile ones are involved because a glass ball coated in cater-pillar flesh is accepted and carried to the centre of the web, but if quinine is added to the coating it is rejected.

The entire sequence of prey-capture in spiders can, therefore, be seen as a series of separate acts, elicited by different releasing stimuli. Many instinctive activities are organised in this way and several examples will be found elsewhere in this book. Courtship behaviour in the Queen butterfly *Danaus gilippus* provides a particularly interesting one because the sequences of responses performed by the male and female are kept in phase with one another. This occurs because each act of one indi-vidual is released by the previous response of the partner and provides the stimuli for the partner's next act (Figure 3). The whole ritual consists of an elaborate chain of responses, cul-minating in copulation, which bears striking analogy with courtship in some vertebrates, such as the Three-spined Stickle-back *Gasterosteus aculeatus*.

Hormones

However, an animal's reaction to a particular releasing situa-tion is not always the same. For example, the responsiveness of virgin female fruitflies, *Drosophila melanogaster*, to males courting them alters with age. After emergence from the pupa, they are unreceptive for several hours, but subsequently re-ceptivity rises and reaches a peak after about three or four days. Thereafter it slowly declines.

Similar cycles of mating behaviour in vertebrates are con-trolled by the secretion of hormones from the endocrine system and there can be little doubt that these substances play essentially the same roles in invertebrates. At present research on this subject is in its infancy, but a connection has already

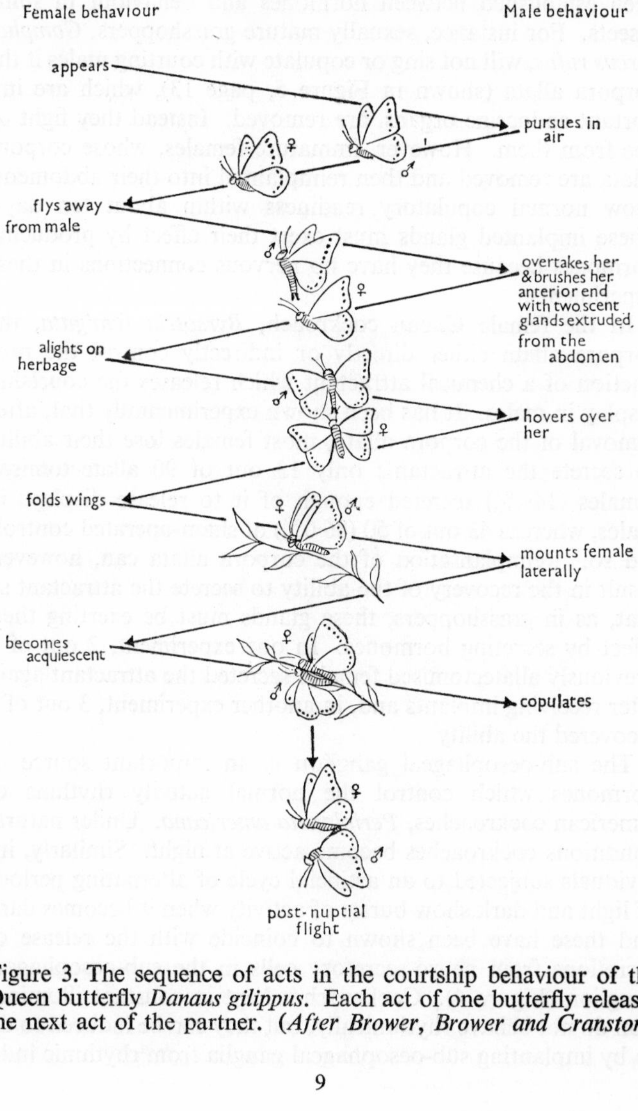

Female behaviour

Male behaviour

appears

pursues in air

flys away from male

overtakes her & brushes her anterior end with two scent glands extruded from the abdomen

alights on herbage

hovers over her

folds wings

mounts female laterally

becomes acquiescent

copulates

post-nuptial flight

Figure 3. The sequence of acts in the courtship behaviour of the Queen butterfly *Danaus gilippus*. Each act of one butterfly releases the next act of the partner. (*After Brower, Brower and Cranston.*)

been established between hormones and behaviour in some insects. For instance, sexually mature grasshoppers, *Gomphocercus rufus*, will not sing or copulate with courting males if the corpora allata (shown in Figure 5, page 13), which are important endocrine organs, are removed. Instead they fight or flee from them. However, immature females, whose corpora allata are removed and then reimplanted into their abdomens, show normal copulatory readiness within about ten days. These implanted glands must exert their effect by producing hormones because they have no nervous connections in these experiments.

In the female Cuban cockroach, *Byrsotria fumigata*, the corpora allata either directly or indirectly control the production of a chemical attractant which releases the courtship display in males. It has been shown experimentally that, after removal of the corpora allata, most females lose their ability to secrete the attractant: only 13 out of 90 allatectomised females (14·4%) secreted enough of it to release displays in males, whereas 43 out of 50 (86·0%) of sham-operated controls did so. Reimplantation of the corpora allata can, however, result in the recovery of the ability to secrete the attractant so that, as in grasshoppers, these glands must be exerting their effect by secreting hormones. In one experiment, 2 out of 6 previously allatectomised females secreted the attractant again after receiving implants and, in another experiment, 3 out of 7 recovered the ability.

The sub-oesophageal ganglion is an important source of hormones which control the normal activity rhythms of American cockroaches, *Periplaneta americana*. Under natural conditions cockroaches become active at night. Similarly, individuals subjected to an artificial cycle of alternating periods of light and dark show bursts of activity when it becomes dark and these have been shown to coincide with the release of secretions from neuro-secretory cells in the sub-oesophageal ganglion (Figure 4). Cockroaches kept in constant illumination do not behave rhythmically, but they can be induced to do so by implanting sub-oesophageal ganglia from rhythmic individuals into their abdomens. Then, for several days afterwards, each recipient follows an activity rhythm which corresponds with that previously performed by the donor.

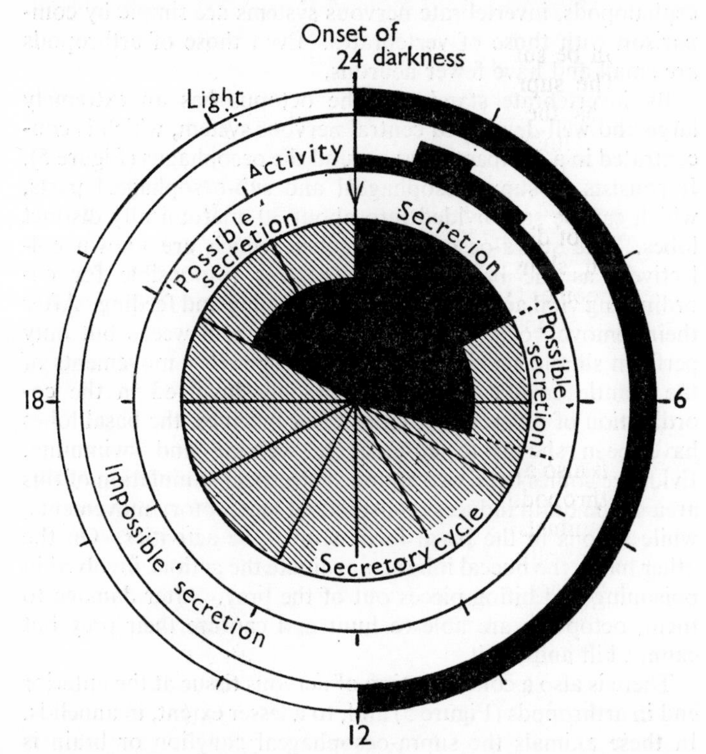

Figure 4. The relationship between release of secretions from the sub-oesophageal ganglion and activity cycles in the cockroach. (*After Harker.*)

The nervous system

Although hormones undoubtedly influence behaviour, the nervous system is ultimately responsible for controlling it. It is difficult to generalise about structures that vary from the diffuse networks of neurons in coelenterates to the more elaborate central nervous systems of some higher invertebrates but, with the possible exception of octopuses and other cephalopods, invertebrate nervous systems are simple by comparison with those of vertebrates. Even those of arthropods are small and have fewer neurons.

By invertebrate standards, the octopus has an extremely large and well-developed central nervous system, which is concentrated in a compact mass around the oesophagus (Figure 5). It consists of supra-oesophageal and sub-oesophageal parts, which can be sub-divided into about 30 anatomically distinct lobes. The supra-oesophageal lobes, which are known collectively as the brain, contain centres responsible for co-ordinating vital activities, such as swimming and feeding. After their removal, octopuses can live for several weeks but only perform simple actions, such as the respiratory movements of the mantle cavity. Different lobes are involved in the co-ordination of different activities. For instance, the basal lobes have been shown to co-ordinate walking and swimming. Evidence comes from two sources: electrical stimulation of this area of the brain induces co-ordinated locomotory movements, while lesions in the basal lobes stop these activities. On the other hand, the buccal lobes co-ordinate the actions involved in poisoning and biting pieces out of the prey. After damage to them, octopuses are able to hunt and capture their prey but cannot kill and eat it.

There is also a concentration of nervous tissue at the anterior end in arthropods (Figure 5) and, to a lesser extent, in annelids. In these animals the supra-oesophageal ganglion or brain is situated dorsally and linked by connectives to a sub-oesophageal ganglion, which is the first in a chain forming the ventral nerve cord. But nervous organisation is simpler than in cephalopods and the brain does not have the same dominance over behaviour. Centres for co-ordinating activities are located in the lower centres of the nervous system so that worms and arthropods are still capable of performing a variety of complex actions after decerebration. For example, extirpa-

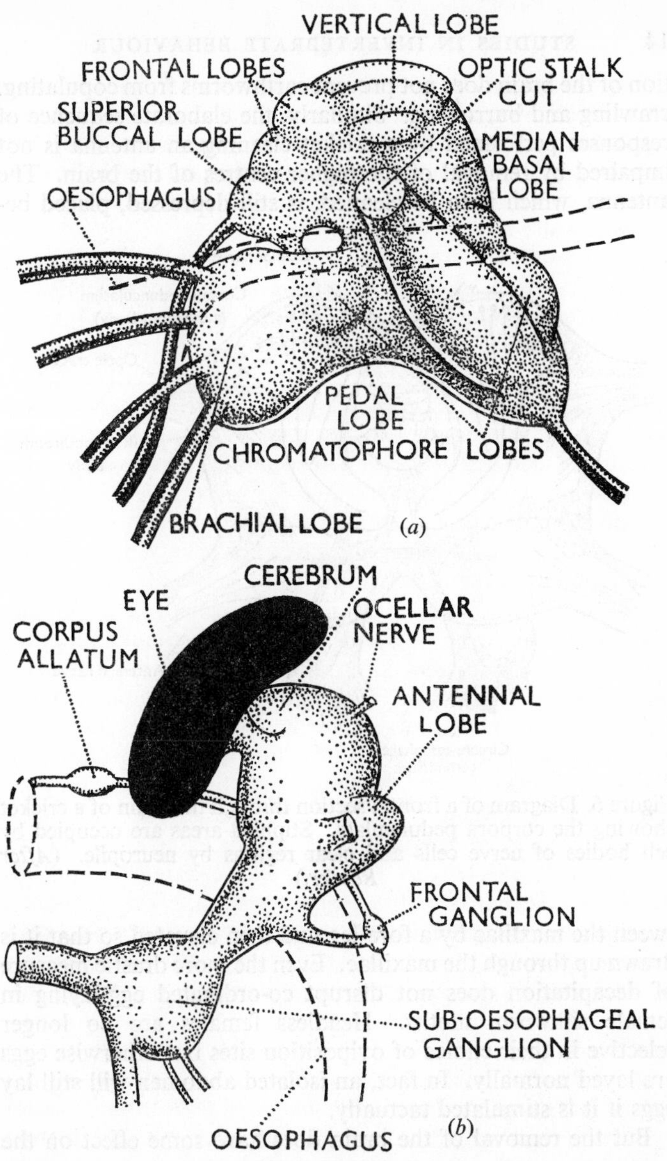

Figure 5. Lateral views of the brains of two invertebrates. (*a*) The brain of an octopus after removal of the large optic lobes. (*After Boycott.*) (*b*) The supra- and sub-oesophageal ganglia of the cockroach. (*After Lawson.*)

tion of the brain does not prevent earthworms from copulating, crawling and burrowing. Similarly, the elaborate sequence of responses performed by a cricket cleaning an antenna is not impaired by removal of the higher centres of the brain. The antenna, which is to be cleaned, is still depressed, placed be-

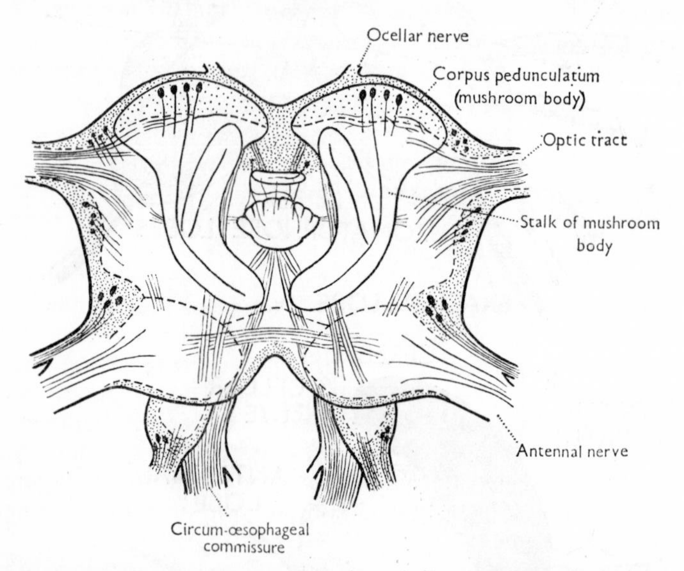

Figure 6. Diagram of a frontal section through the brain of a cricket showing the corpora pedunculata. Stippled areas are occupied by cell bodies of nerve cells and clear regions by neuropile. (*After Roeder.*)

tween the maxillae by a fore-leg and then elevated so that it is drawn up through the maxillae. Even the more drastic measure of decapitation does not disrupt co-ordinated egg-laying in female silkworm moths. Headless females are no longer selective in their choice of oviposition sites but otherwise eggs are layed normally. In fact, an isolated abdomen will still lay eggs if it is stimulated tactually.

But the removal of the brain does have some effect on the

activities of annelids and arthropods. It results in general hyperactivity in the ragworm *Nereis diversicolor* and decerebrate worms crawl or swim about incessantly. Similarly decapitation releases unusually vigorous and continuous copulatory movements in the male praying mantis. Curiously enough, this may even be of survival value to mantids. A female sometimes attacks and devours her mate, particularly if she is disturbed during courtship. But, since the male faces the female as he approaches her, his head is seized and eaten first and, even after this treatment, he is capable of mounting and successfully copulating with her.

It is also possible to release whole patterns of behaviour by electrical or mechanical stimulation of the brains of some insects. For example, stimulation of parts of the characteristically mushroom-shaped bodies, the corpora pedunculata, in the brains of crickets (Figure 6) induces the continuous performance of courtship or threat stridulation, in which the hind femora is rubbed against a prominent vein in each tegmina. Stimulation of similar sites in the brains of honeybees evokes actions such as cleaning and aggression. It seems likely, therefore, that centres in the brain are responsible for regulating the excitability of behaviour mechanisms, in the sense of modifying their thresholds, intensity and duration, without co-ordinating their components.

The corpora pedunculata are particularly well developed in the Hymenoptera and, within this order of insects, there is a rough correlation between the complexity of these lobes and the elaboration of behaviour. For example, the corpora have attained a greater size and development in the social species, such as honeybees, which have particularly rich repertoires of behaviour, than non-social species, such as saw-flies. But even in these animals the overall size of the central nervous system is remarkably small. It is amazing that such functional complexity has been achieved by such a small amount of nervous tissue.

2

Courtship Displays and Aggression

The complex courtship ceremonies of many animals provide some of the most interesting examples of instinctive behaviour. Those of vertebrates, particularly birds, have received the most attention, but some invertebrates also perform elaborate rituals before mating. In these animals the sexes are often easy to distinguish and often some part of the anatomy, such as the enlarged claw in male fiddler crabs or the plumage of many birds, becomes specially modified so that it can be displayed prominently. However, not all animals court before copulating. Many fish and marine worms merely shed their gametes into the water, where fertilisation takes place. But, even in these animals, there is usually some synchronisation of the release of gametes and in some of them the timing is extremely precise.

Synchronisation of reproductive behaviour in polychteae worms

Male and female polychaetes are usually indistinguishable in their appearance and generally release their eggs and sperms externally so that contact is largely fortuitous. However, several mechanisms enhance the chances of successful fertilisation. Some polychaetes leave their burrows to make impressive spawning migrations to the surface of the sea. Sometimes they collect in huge swarms, which are famous for their precise timing. The Atlantic palolo worm *Eunice fucata*, for instance, swarms on two, three and sometimes four consecutive nights close to the third lunar quarter in July, although, if this is late in the month, they may spawn at the first quarter.

In fact it is only the posterior halves of the palolo worms that swim to the surface. These become specially modified to form so-called epitokes, which break free from the anterior ends and spawn. The important external stimulus that elicits spawning appears to be the intensity of lunar illumination. Epitokes are photopositive when the light intensity is between 0·005- and 50-foot candles, whereas the anterior ends of worms are photonegative to intensities greater than 0·01 foot candles. By July the worms are ready to spawn, but for most of the time the light conditions are unsuitable. At full moon and in daylight the worms withdraw from the intense light and are confined to the burrows and at new moon, there is not enough light to attract the epitokes. However, at the first and third quarters, the intensity of moonlight is still below the threshold for photonegative behaviour of the anterior end and, yet, there is enough for the photopositive reaction of the epitokes. As a result, corkscrew movements begin, which detach the two halves. The epitokes then swim to the surface and spawn.

The ragworm *Nereis succinea* also swarms at the surface of the sea but spawning only occurs in the presence of a suitable mate. The males, which swarm first, respond to the appearance of a female by swimming around them in narrowing circles. Gametes are shed after mutual stimulation from worms of opposite sexes; a chemical stimulant emanating from the female initiates the release of sperms by the male whereas females spawn in response to sperms in the water. The circling dance of a male and sperm emission can be evoked in the absence of a female but only if he is placed in sea water from which a mature female, or her eggs, has been removed. Females, which already have spawned, evoke no response although, four or five spent females, kept in a small quantity of water overnight, induced a weak nuptial dance in a mature male given access to them the following morning. Mating with related species of *Nereis* is prevented because the chemical stimulus needed to elicit gamete release in the male is highly specific; males will not react to females or eggs of other species.

Sexual isolation in fiddler crabs

Arthropods, with well developed eyes, often recognise their mates visually and many of them court actively before copulating. However, the function of courtship is not always obvious and it is certainly not necessarily a prerequisite of successful mating. Males of the fruit-fly *Drosophila* court vigorously, but in the related fly *Sarcophaga* a male approaches a female and attempts to copulate with her without any display or formality.

A satisfactory explanation of the function of courtship in fiddler crabs is that it enables species, which intermingle on the same beach, to remain sexually isolated because females can identify males of the same species by their characteristic displays. The male fiddler crabs construct burrows on flat shores and attract females by waving movements of the enlarged claw. The beckoning behaviour varies in details from species to species, but there appear to be two main types of display. A typical claw movement in the so-called 'broad-front' fiddler crabs is seen in *Uca lactea*, in which the claw is moved in a high arc over the body; it travels laterally and upwards and is then suddenly retracted (Figure 7). In the 'narrow-front' fiddler crabs, such as *Uca rhizophorae*, the large claw is moved vertically up to about eye level and then down again, but it is not extended laterally. Apart from differences in claw beckoning, male behaviour in related species may differ in other ways. For example, *Uca pugnax* males bow once or twice in front of the female during their display, whereas the related *Uca rapax* males do not bow at all. Similarly males of *Uca beebei* turn around in front of the female during courtship while males of *Uca stenodactyla* run to and fro between beckoning phases of courtship. Female fiddler crabs do not display, but they may approach several different displaying males before eventually mating with one of them.

During the performance of instinctive patterns of behaviour by vertebrates, apparently irrelevant acts, known as displacement activities, are sometimes observed. These usually occur in conflict situations, that is, when opposing needs of the animal are simultaneously aroused. Male sticklebacks, for

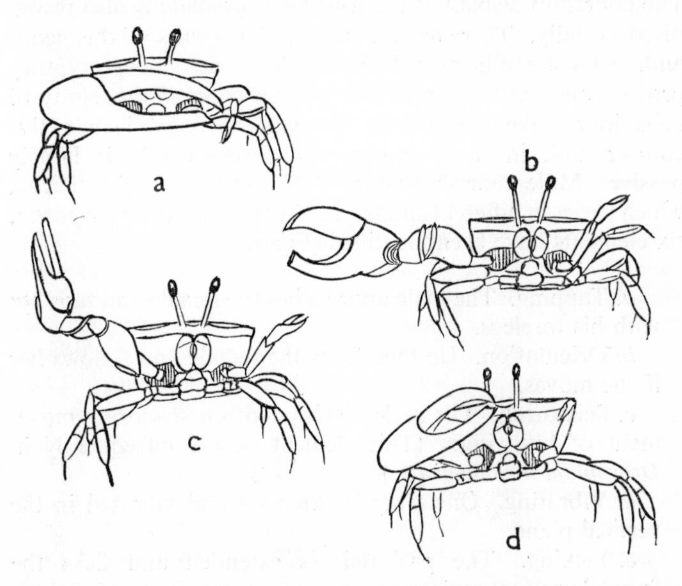

Figure 7. The broad-front courtship display of the fiddler crab *Uca lactea*. The enlarged claw is raised from the starting position (*a*), flexed outwards (*b*), raised upwards (*c*) and returned to the starting position (*d*). (*After Crane.*)

instance, often dig in the sand when there is a conflict between attacking a rival male and fleeing from him. Fiddler crabs perform displacement activities in similar situations. For example, male *Uca festae* sometimes buff and polish the large claw with the smaller one when there is a conflict between fleeing from a human observer and courting a mate. In similar circumstances, *Uca lactea* may perform displacement feeding, in which the crab goes through the motions of feeding without ingesting any food.

Selection of a mate in the fruit-fly Drosophila

The courtship display of the fruit-fly *Drosophila* is also recognised visually. There are more than 600 species of this genus and, as most can be reared successfully in the laboratory, they provide an excellent opportunity for a comparative study of behaviour. Like fiddler crabs, the male *Drosophila* is the active courter and, in most species, the female's role is largely passive. Male courtship consists of a sequence of activities, which varies in different species, but in *Drosophila melanogaster*, six elements have been identified (Figure 8):

a. Tapping. The male approaches the female and taps her with his forelegs.
b. Orientation. He then faces the female and follows her if she moves.
c. Scissoring. The male displays with a scissoring movement of his wings. (This element occurs infrequently in *Drosophila melanogaster*.)
d. Vibrating. One wing is extended and vibrated in the vertical plane.
e. Licking. The proboscis is extended and licks the female's genital region.
f. Attempted copulation. The male curls his abdomen down and forward and attempts to mount the female.

A receptive female spreads her genital plates and her wings to facilitate mounting, but an unreceptive female shows a variety of repelling movements, flicking the wings, kicking backwards with the hind legs, extending the ovipositor and jumping or moving rapidly away. Courtship in other species of *Drosophila* is different from that in *Drosophila melanogaster*, but there are usually obvious similarities. For example, the same elements occur in the courtship of *Drosophila sub-obscura* but, in this species, both the males and the otherwise passive females perform a side-stepping dance as part of the routine. There may also be differences in the sequence of the courtship elements in different species. Male *Drosophila melanogaster* perform them in the order *a–b–c–d–e–f*, although scissoring *c* is

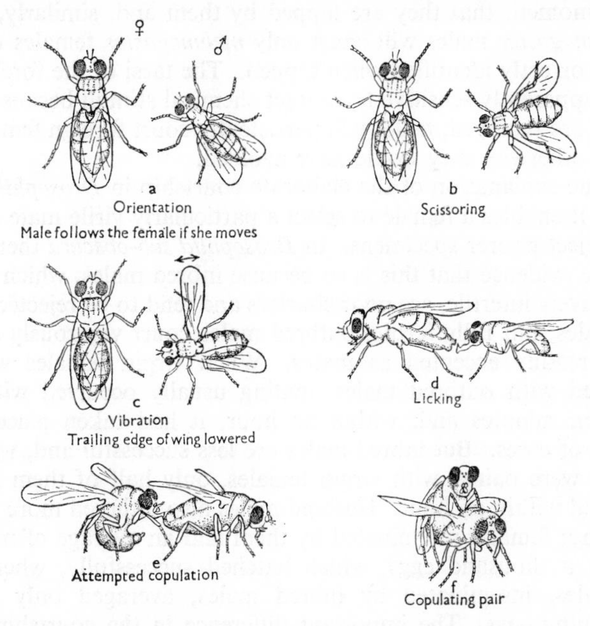

Figure 8. Successive elements in the courtship display of the male fruit-fly *Drosophila melanogaster*. (*After Manning*.)

usually omitted. But in *Drosophila auraria*, *D. rufa* and *D. montium* the sequence is *a–b–e–f–d*; the males actually mount and attempt to copulate before they vibrate their wings. There are also differences in the manner in which some of the elements are performed; the speed of wing vibration is 250–300 c/s in *D. pessimilis*, but faster, 450–550 c/s, in *D. pseudo-obscura*.

But, unlike the courtship displays in fiddler crabs, differences in the visual components of male displays are not a means whereby a female recognises a mate of her own species. Recognition of a suitable mate usually occurs at the outset of courtship when the male taps the female with his forelegs. Female *Drosophila simulans* reject *D. melanogaster* males from the moment that they are tapped by them and, similarly, *D. melanogaster* males will court only *melanogaster* females that are correctly identified when tapped. The tarsi of the forelegs are apparently sensitive to contact chemical stimuli because, if they are removed, males will persistently court foreign females that otherwise they would have avoided.

One explanation of the elaborate courtship in *Drosophila* is that it enables a female to select a particularly virile mate and to reject poorer specimens. In *Drosophila sub-obscura* there is some evidence that this is so because inbred males, which are relatively infertile, are poor courters and tend to be rejected by females, but fully fertile, outbred males court vigorously and are readily accepted as mates. When virgin females were paired with outbred males, mating usually occurred within fifteen minutes and, within an hour, it had taken place in 90% of cases. But inbred males are less successful and, when they were paired with virgin females, only half of them had mated within an hour. Outbred males also fathered more off-spring; females inseminated by them laid an average of more than a thousand eggs, which hatched successfully, whereas females, inseminated by inbred males, averaged only 264 hatching eggs. The important difference in the courtship of inbred and outbred male *Drosophila sub-obscura* appears to be in the orientation response and the side-stepping dance, which is characteristic of this species. When the male orientates him-self to face the female, she responds by dancing rapidly from one side to the other and is followed by the male, which also dances. If the male can keep up with the female and continues to face her during the dance, he is usually accepted and copula-tion follows. Outbred males normally court successfully, but inbred males often fail to keep the position facing the female during the dance and are, consequently, rejected as mates.

Co-ordination of courtship in scorpions

Elaborate courtship also occurs in some invertebrates in which there is transference of a sperm packet (spermatophore) from male to female. Co-ordination of courtship is necessary so that the spermatophore can be successfully transferred. There are no obvious differences in the sexes in the scorpion *Parabuthus planicanda* but males seem to have little difficulty in recognising females because they will not court other males. During courtship the male grips the female's pedipalps with his own and then drags her about with him as he investigates the surface of the soil to find a site suitable for the deposition of a spermatophore. Meanwhile he may make movements that probably passify the female into co-operation, such as 'juddering', which consists of 5 to 8 rapid forward and backward movements of the body while the legs remain still. When the male finds a suitable place, and the female is in the necessary passive state, he extrudes the spermatophore and then pulls the female across it in a series of jerks so that the sperms pass into her genital ducts. He then releases her and the pair separate.

The appeasement function of courtship in some spiders

Some of the most elaborate courtship displays are performed by spiders of the genus *Corythalia.* Those spiders do not build webs but stalk and pounce on their prey. An important function of the male's display is, therefore, to introduce himself to the female without arousing her predatory responses. His display is usually performed at a distance and consists of a complex visual signalling system. A male of the species *Corythalia xanthopa*, for instance, signals his approach by rocking from side to side and then extending his forelegs forwards at an angle of about 45° to the ground (Figure 9). A receptive female sometimes gives a weak reciprocal display and then adopts a position in which she crouches and draws her legs in.

The displays of males of different species have their own characteristics. A male *Corythalia fulgipeda*, for instance, jerks his palps in unison and intermittently raises and vibrates his third pair of legs. In another species, *Corythalia chalcea*, the

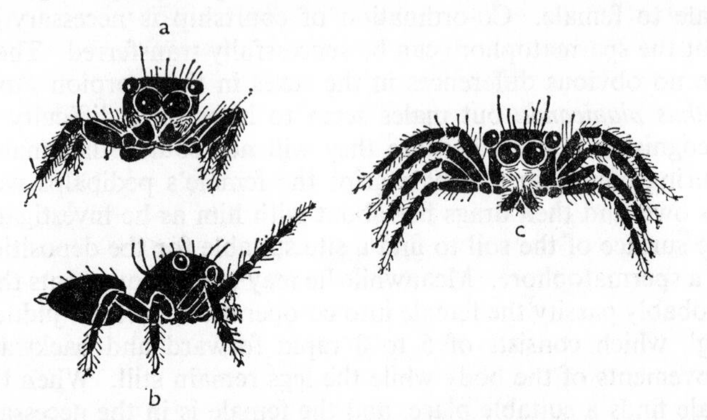

Figure 9. Courtship and aggressive postures in the male spider *Corythalia xanthopa*. (*a*) Frontal view of rocking, which is a prelude to the courtship display. (*b*) Side view of courtship posture; the anterior legs are raised at an angle of 45°. (*c*) Frontal view of the threat display. (*After Crane.*)

palps of the male hang motionless during the display but the third pair of legs is stretched out and waved up and down. Females are able to recognise males of their own species by their displays and are only receptive to them. Males are, however, less discriminating and will start to display to females of related species as well as their own.

Aggression and territorial behaviour

Sexually mature males often refuse to tolerate the nearby presence of rival males and will attack them. However, as in vertebrates, fights are usually ritualised. The combatants go through a series of displays before fighting, but one usually backs away during the initial display phase so that the contest is settled without injury to either winner or loser. Presumably this is advantageous to the species as a whole because it ensures that immature males, which have not had the opportunity to breed, are not damaged by the more mature and more aggressive individuals. A typical display is that of the male cuttlefish *Sepia.* The striped, zebra pattern on the sides of his body becomes intensified when he is approached by another cuttlefish. If the display is returned the approaching cuttlefish is recognised as a male. Two males manoeuvre to lie side by side but, generally, the smaller and less brilliant one 'fades' and swims away before there is any aggression.

There is a rough correlation between the elaboration of threat displays and the potential damage that animals can inflict upon one another. Spiders of the genus *Corythalia,* for example, which are carnivorous and have poisonous jaws, have highly ritualised displays. Concomitantly, actual fighting between individuals is rarely observed. Displaying males of the species *Corythalia xanthopa* raise their bodies off the ground and hold the second, third and fourth pairs of legs progressively higher (Figure 9). At the same time the palps are flexed so that yellow scales on them make a continuous band with the area of yellow coloration on the face. Apparently this band enables a male to recognise an approaching male and distinguish him from females. Normally a male confronted with his own image in a mirror displays aggressively to it, but if his palps are removed he reacts to his image as if it was a female and courts it.

Threat displays between animals, such as gryllid field crickets, which are less capable of inflicting damage, are usually less elaborate. However, most encounters are still settled without violence. Dr. R. A. Alexander recognises five levels of encounter in crickets (Table 1). Most contests are settled at third level encounters in which the fore- or hind-body may be reared and the legs kicked, but there are no aggressive acts. In the few intense ones that occur there may be sparring with the forelegs, butting with the head, grappling, wrestling and biting, but even as a result of these fights the loser rarely suffers much physical damage. Contests are settled more by tenacity and ferocity than by fighting ability.

Among groups of male gryllid crickets a status system of dominance is often established which bears analogy with the peck order in social vertebrates. Each male tends to win nearly all of his encounters with males below him in the hierarchy, but tends to lose to males above him and, as in vertebrates, encounters between rivals in similar positions in the hierarchy are usually more intense than those between males far apart.

TABLE 1

The levels of fighting encounters in gryllid crickets based on 1042 observations (after Alexander)

Level of encounters	*Description of behaviour*	*Percentage of encounters settled at each level*
First Level	Contact terminated without clear dominance by either individual. There is no aggression.	7
Second Level	One individual retreats but there is no aggression.	26
Third Level	Contact settled after mild aggression.	56
Fourth Level	Contact terminated after moderate aggression.	7
Fifth Level	Contact terminated after sustained combat.	4

Territorial behaviour has been observed in male field crickets, which occupy crevices. They patrol the surrounding area and fight any males that are encountered in it. A male is particularly aggressive in his own territory but is far less aggressive outside it. This can lead to an almost complete reversal of dominance in males in adjacent territories. In one reported instance a male which defeated another in all thirteen of the observed encounters in his own territory won only a single contest out of 20 in his neighbour's territory.

It is probable that territorial behaviour prevents overcrowding of individuals and may give aggressive males a better chance of finding a mate.

3

Feeding

Almost all invertebrates react instinctively to their food. Generally they recognise it by sight or smell although some, such as spiders, which respond to vibrations caused by struggling prey in their webs, detect it by mechanical means. However, visual recognition is confined mainly to arthropods and some molluscs, which have well developed eyes. Although many invertebrates are sensitive to light, their light receptors do not form images and, consequently, they depend upon other sorts of stimuli for food detection.

Feeding in coelenterates

Sessile coelenterates, such as sea anemones and *Hydra*, recognise food by a combination of mechanical and chemical means. Their feeding behaviour consists of a sequence of activities in which small animals or animal remains are captured by the tentacles, conveyed by them to the centre of the oral disc and pushed into the mouth. Prey is held by the harpoon-like nematocysts in the tentacles which are fired when they are stimulated by food. The actual stimulus that triggers the nematocysts in the snakelocks anemone, *Anemonia sulcata*, is mechanical, but relatively few are fired by this stimulus on its own because the threshold of stimulation is high. However, the threshold is lowered by the presence of substances associated with food, such as animal body fluids or mucus, so that, although non-nutritive objects fire few of them, large numbers are discharged when food comes into contact with the tentacles.

There is a remarkable range in the function of nematocysts

in *Hydra*, which employs them in locomotion and defence, as well as in feeding. There are four kinds, all of which are fired by mechanical stimulation, but can contribute to different aspects of the animal's behaviour because their thresholds to stimulation are normally high and are only lowered under specific conditions. The feeding and defensive nematocysts are only fired in large numbers in the presence of certain substances that lower their mechanical thresholds. Two kinds, the *stenoteles* and *desmonemes* are employed in food capture and, like anemone nematocysts, the effective substances are those associated with food. Defensive nematocysts, *holotrichous isorhizas*, are fired against noxious or non-nutritive animals, such as the flatworm *Polycelis* and, in this case, it is substances produced by these animals that lower the threshold. For instance, in the presence of slime from *Polycelis*, *holotrichous isorhizas* are fired in large numbers by mechanical stimulation. The fourth type, *atrichous isorhizas*, are important in the characteristic somersaulting locomotion of *Hydra* and enable the tentacles to adhere to the substratum while the 'foot' is moved to a new position. In one experiment, glass rods, coated in a non-nutritive silica gel and held in contact with the tentacles of *Hydra vulgaris attenuata* for 30 seconds, fired *atrichous isorhizas* in 16 out of 20 attempts, but similar rods, coated in a crustacean food extract, elicited responses in only 1 out of 20 attempts. The explanation of these results seems to be that these nematocysts are fired by contact with solid objects when the animal is moving, but are not triggered when the tentacles are capturing food because the presence of food substances actually raises their threshold of stimulation.

In *Anemonia* the tentacular response, by which captured food is conveyed to the mouth, can also be elicited by mechanical stimulation, but without simultaneous chemical stimulation from food substances there is not sustained excitation and non-nutritive objects are rejected by the tentacles. Balls of cotton wool soaked in various solutions and placed on the tentacles may be taken to the mouth or rejected, depending upon their chemical nature. Proteins, presented to

Anemonia in this way, are usually effective in eliciting a positive response of the tentacles and are taken to the mouth, but carbohydrates are relatively ineffective. For example, 1% egg white elicits a positive tentacular response, but much higher concentrations of the sugars, maltose and glucose, do not. Mouth opening, which occurs in preparation for the receipt of the food, is also elicited by chemical stimulation, but the threshold of this response is lower than that of the tentacles. A preparation of 0·01% egg white acts as a sufficiently strong stimulus and the sugars, maltose and glucose, which did not elicit a tentacular response, induced mouth opening, although only in relatively concentrated amounts.

Chemical stimulation is also important to the feeding *Hydra*. The tripeptide glutathione is a particularly effective stimulant and will elicit persistent feeding responses in *Hydra littoralis*, although its effectiveness is related to the time since the animal was last fed. Whereas 10^{-6} M solutions of glutathione elicited writhing of the tentacles and mouth opening in *Hydra* starved for 8 days, there was only tentacle writhing in animals starved for 2 days and no response at all in more recently fed hydras. Glutathione is a common constituent of animal tissues and, for example, leaks from the water flea *Daphnia*, which is a common prey of *Hydra*, when it is damaged by the nematocysts. *Hydra littoralis* feeds almost exclusively on animals which have coelomic body fluids, because only these release enough glutathione to initiate feeding and, consequently, lower invertebrates and inanimate objects are not generally accepted as food. But if a solution of glutathione is added to the water, *Hydra* no longer discriminates; it may become cannibalistic or make abortive attempts to swallow the glass wall of its container, resulting in either total or partial inversion of the animal.

Activity cycles

When the behaviour of an animal, such as a coelenterate, is analysed in the laboratory it sometimes gives the impression that it can be explained simply in terms of reflex responses to stimuli. But this is an over-simplification. Animals are probably never completely in a state of rest but in continually changing states of activity, and it is against this background that their behaviour should be considered. By attaching

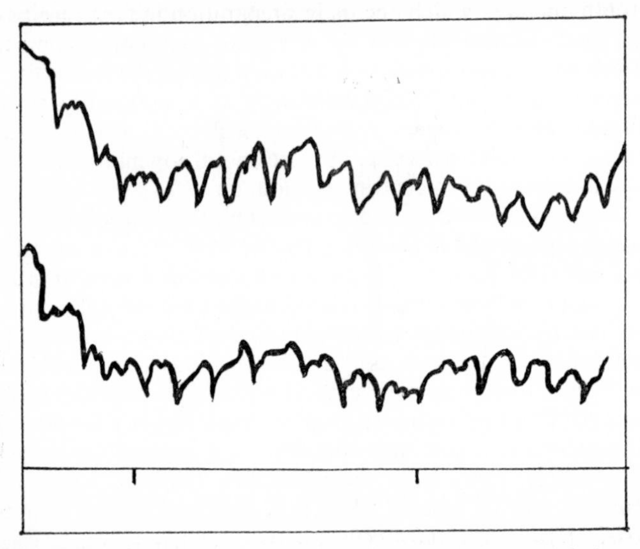

Figure 10. Spontaneous contractions and relaxations of the sea anemone *Metridium* recorded by two isotonic levers attached to points on the body wall. The time interval shown on the record is one hour. (*After Pantin.*)

recording levers to the column of the sea anemone *Metridium* Professor C. F. A. Pantin and Dr. E. J. Bantham have shown that the animal is continually active, even when it is not stimulated by external events. Slow, rhythmic contractions and extensions, which often alternate at intervals of about 10 minutes, apparently originate within the organism itself because they occur without reference to external stimulation due to changes in illumination, temperature or vibration (Figure 10). The addition of food extract affects the activity of the anemone.

After an extract of one part in a million of dried mussel was added to the sea water containing an anemone the same alternations of contraction and extension continued, but the extension phases were relatively more pronounced (Figure 11). The effect was that the anemone elongated and it remained like this for four hours after the original stimulation from the food

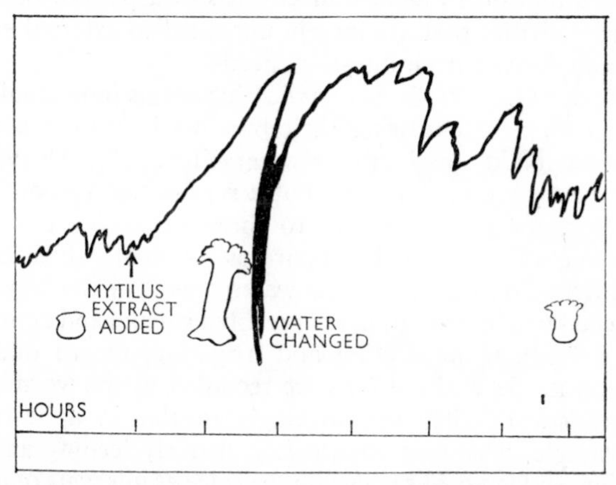

Figure 11. The effect of the addition of mussel (*Mytilis*) extract on the activity of the sea anemone *Metridium*. Recordings made by isotonic levers attached to the anemone. The outline figures illustrate the shape of the animal at different stages. (*After Pantin.*)

extract even though the water was changed for clean sea water after two hours. Elongation undoubtedly increases the anemone's chances of discovering food that has stimulated it chemically, but has not touched the tentacles; occasional, slow, swaying movements of the column, which sometimes appeared, presumably serve the same end.

Spontaneous cycles of activity are also an important component of the behaviour of the lugworm, *Arenicola marina*, which lives in permanent U-shaped burrows in muddy sand. Lugworms feed on mud at the bottom of the head shaft of the burrow and irrigate it by means of peristaltic movements of the body that drive a current of water through it. The central nervous system of *Arenicola* is not well developed and consequently one might expect that its behaviour would consist of a few simple reflex responses: feeding to an empty stomach, defaecation to a full rectum, and irrigation to the presence of deoxygenated water in the burrow. But this is not so. In its burrow a lugworm's behaviour consists of a pattern of spontaneous activities that are largely unrelated to external events or stimuli derived from intestinal needs.

Professor G. P. Wells has studied lugworms individually by allowing them to construct their burrows in special aquaria containing muddy sand and sea water (Figure 12). The worms cannot be seen in the burrows, but it is possible to record their behaviour, for periods of up to three weeks, by observing movements of water in the apparatus. A float, which is displaced by the movements of the water caused by the lugworm, is attached to a lever writing on a revolving drum and activities, such as feeding, defaecating and irrigating, record different traces on it. Several patterns are recorded by the worms, but characteristically they are strikingly regular in appearance. For example, whenever *Arenicola* is actively feeding and defaecating, sudden peaks occur on the trace at intervals of about 35 minutes. They correspond with the release of faeces and are due to the large displacement of water caused by the lugworm crawling backwards up the tail shaft of its burrow to deposit the faecal caste on the surface of the sand. Similarly, movements due to bursts of feeding activity are traced at intervals of 7–8 minutes between the defaecation peaks. Both defaecation and feeding are spontaneous, rather than reflex, activities because lugworms kept in glass tubes, in which their behaviour can be observed, show similar bursts of feeding activity, when no food is available, and regular defaecating excursions, when there are no faeces to be voided.

These activities are apparently controlled by pacemakers or 'physiological clocks' in the nervous system, which trigger them at regular intervals. The feeding cycle pacemaker is probably located in a plexus of nervous tissue around the oesophagus.

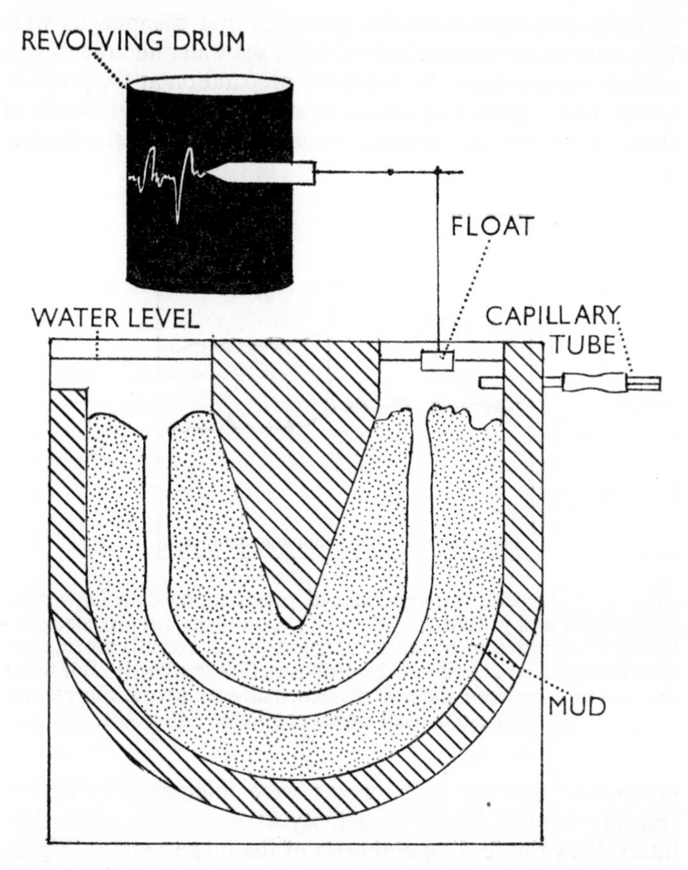

Figure 12. A diagram of the apparatus used to record the behaviour of a lugworm living in mud. The approximate outline of a worm's burrow is indicated in the mud. Activities of the worm, such as feeding, irrigating and defaecating cause movements of water which displace the float. This is attached to a recording lever writing on a revolving drum. Various activities can be recognised by the characteristic recordings. (*After Wells.*)

Isolated preparations of the proboscis and oesophagus were kept alive in the worm's body fluid or sea water and recordings of their activity made by fixing the preparation at the junction of the two organs and attaching recording levers to each of them. Evidently this isolated preparation includes the feeding

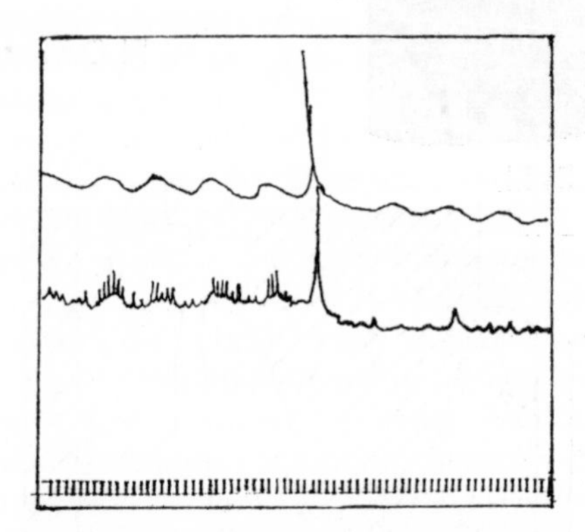

Figure 13. Recordings from isolated preparations of a lugworm's oesophagus and proboscis. When the two organs are attached outbursts of contraction of the oesophagus (upper record) correspond with outbursts of activity of the proboscis (lower record). But when the junction between them is severed, half-way across the record, only the oesophageal waves continue. (*After Wells.*)

pacemaker because both organs were intermittently active, showing regular bursts of activity at about the same time intervals as the feeding outbursts of the intact worms (Figure 13). A further experiment showed that the pacemaker is located in the oesophagus. When the junction between the proboscis and oesophagus was severed the oesophageal bursts of activity continued, whereas those of the proboscis ceased. Apparently the pacemaker in the oesophagus 'drives' the proboscis when the lugworm feeds.

Sequential nature of feeding behaviour

Like many instinctive activities, feeding behaviour usually consists of a sequence of responses, and even the relatively simple animals, such as sea anemones, perform several acts before food is ingested. However, feeding in the lower invertebrates is generally elicited by relatively unspecific stimuli; for example, the entire sequence can be induced in *Anemonia* by any one of a variety of different food substances coupled with mechanical stimulation. Similarly in *Hydra* the feeding releaser glutathione is unspecific because it is a constituent of almost all animal tissues. But the situation becomes increasingly complex in higher invertebrates. Several stimuli may be needed before food is accepted and often the sequence of activities is arranged hierarchically, with each response in the series elicited by a different stimulus.

In some animals, such as planarians, which are guided to their food by chemoreception, the stimuli are similar in nature but differ in intensity. Two responses are released by chemical stimulation emanating from dead animal matter, but the responses occur in sequence because one is released by weak stimulation when food is first detected, and the other by stronger stimulation when the food is approached. Weak stimuli, which are detected by chemoreceptors located on lobes on each side of the anterior end of the worm, initiate a positive food seeking response towards the source of stimulation. The planarian moves towards the food because it keeps on a straight course when the lobes at the anterior end are equally stimulated by food substances. If an open-ended U-tube, filled with animal extract, is drawn in front of a planarian so that the fluids are released at equal distances from the lobes, the planarian moves in a straight line towards the centre of the tube and not towards either of the sources of stimulation (Figure 14). But at some point when the animal is close to the food, other chemoreceptors located on the proboscis are stimulated by the stronger stimulation, and actual feeding then replaces the seeking behaviour.

Some arthropods perform an extremely elaborate sequence of responses before feeding. For example, hunting behaviour of the waterboatman, *Notonecta glauca*, consists of an impressive sequence of activities, each released by a specific stimulus. Vibrations, such as those caused by insects falling on to the surface of the water, initiate the first response in the sequence. The waterboatman reacts by taking position with

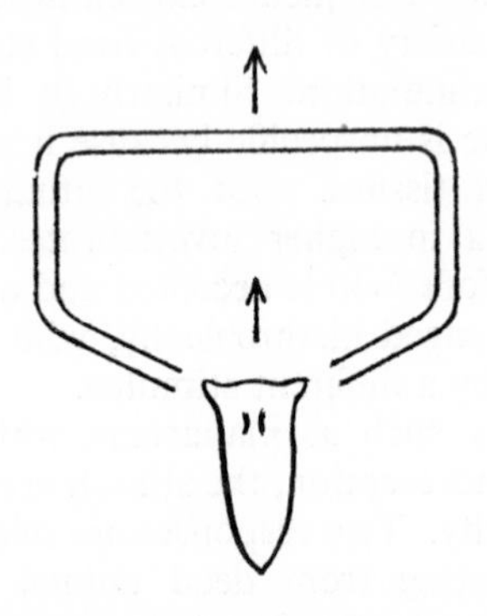

Figure 14. An open-ended U-tube, filled with snail's blood, which can be used to stimulate the two sets of chemoreceptors on the lobes at the anterior end of a planarian. If these lobes are stimulated simultaneously, the worm moves between the two sources of stimulation.

the tips of the first and second pairs of legs and its abdomen against the surface film and, in this way, is able to perceive the vibrations from a distance as far as 20 cm. When these are not too strong or too weak, the animal orientates itself in that direction and swims towards the source of vibrations. Within 5 cm of the source the behaviour changes; *Notonecta* swings its third pair of legs powerfully backwards and falls on the prey. However, this time it is a visual stimulus that releases the response, because if a wire is used to make the vibrations, the waterboatman will approach it but will attack a nearby moving object rather than the wire (Figure 15). The explana-

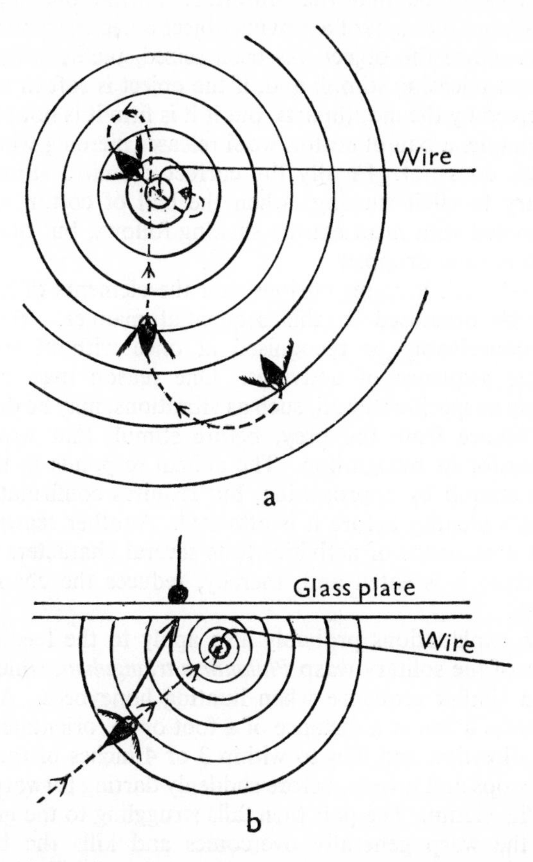

Figure 15. Feeding behaviour of the waterboatman *Notonecta*. (*a*) The animal orientates itself and swims to the source of vibrations caused by a wire dipped into the surface of the water. (*b*) It attacks a small moving object on the other side of a glass plate rather than the wire. (*After Baerends*.)

tion seems to be that the vibrations release the approach response, but the sight of a moving object is necessary to release capture. Once the object has been seized, tactile stimuli are important releasing stimuli and, if the object is soft in texture, it is pierced by the mouthparts, but if it is firm it is not pierced. For example, a ball of cotton wool releases piercing whereas a wax ball does not. Finally the correct chemical stimuli are necessary to elicit sucking; when the ball of cotton wool is impregnated with meat extract sucking follows, but otherwise the ball is soon dropped.

At first sight it seems curious that the elements of hunting should be organised in this sequential manner. The prey might conceivably be recognised at once without such an elaborate sequence of activities. One reason may be that relatively unspecific stimuli, such as vibrations, may be detected at a distance from the prey, before stimuli that would be adequate for its recognition. The animal responds to the unspecific stimuli by approaching, but requires confirmation of the prey's identity before it is attacked. Another reason may be that a sequence of activities tests several characters of the prey before it is eaten and, thereby, reduces the chances of mistakes.

These explanations probably also apply to the feeding behaviour of the solitary wasp *Philanthus triangulum*, which performs a similar sequence when hunting honeybees. A wasp first locates a bee at a distance of a foot or so, orientates itself in that direction and flies to within 3 or 4 inches of the prey. It then stops and hovers, before suddenly darting forwards and seizing its victim. The pair then falls struggling to the ground, where the wasp generally overcomes and kills the bee by stinging it beneath the head.

Philanthus approaches and 'hovers-at' almost any object that is about the size of a honeybee, including other insects such as bumblebees and flies, so that the initial response to its prey is almost certainly released by visual stimuli. Indeed, this was confirmed in an experimental investigation in which it was shown that dead bees and pieces of wood of about the same size, suspended on fine threads and made to move slightly, were also inspected as potential prey. However, wasps will only attack objects which have the odour of live honeybees. Presumably this is picked up during the hovering flight. They will seize suspended sticks, which have been shaken with live honeybees to give them the correct odour, but soon lose interest in unscented sticks or preserved, and therefore de-odorised, bees. But other stimuli, probably visual or tactile ones, are needed to release the stinging response because, although scented sticks are captured, no attempt is made to sting them.

When invertebrates become highly specific in their feeding requirements the sequential arrangement of responses may persist, but the releasing stimuli often become specific and fit the food-object more closely. For example, the only known stimulus that invariably elicits a feeding response in newly hatched cuttlefish *Sepia* is the sight of the crustacean *Mysis*. Recognition of the prey is undoubtedly visual because mysids enclosed in glass tubes are attacked as readily as free swimming ones.

Cuttlefish attacking for the first time have been tested with moving models painted on to Perspex cylinders, but are generally unreactive to them. Even one resembling a real *Mysis* only induced attacks in 7 out of 38 *Sepia* tested. But the food of cuttlefish is not always restricted to *Mysis*. With more experience, the releasing stimuli needed to evoke attack become less specific and, therefore, the range of models that will elicit feeding responses increases until a cuttlefish attacking for the tenth or twentieth time stabs at almost anything that moves. Concomitantly there is an increase in the variety of animals preyed upon.

Random searching behaviour of ladybird larvae

In contrast to *Sepia* and the arthropods considered in this chapter, ladybird larvae are incapable of detecting their prey at a distance of even 5 cm. Nevertheless, they feed successfully, probably because of the abundance of aphids on which they prey and behaviour patterns that keep them in an area rich in aphids once one is encountered. Newly hatched larvae, which must find food within 24 hours of hatching if they are to survive, make random searching movements on plants and they may cover the same area more than once. However, when chance contact is made with aphids their behaviour changes. The larvae now make numerous turns from side to side, which are also random, but enable them to search the area adjacent to the original victim (Figure 16). Aphids congregate on plants in groups so that this behaviour increases their chances of finding more food. The success of this searching behaviour was demonstrated by placing larvae of the ladybird *Adalia bipunctata* on cards to which aphids had been fixed. One *Adalia* larva found and devoured one aphid and then made small turns which eventually brought it into contact with the other eight aphids on the card. When all the aphids had been eaten further searching was unrewarded and the behaviour reverted to the before-feeding, wide, random movements.

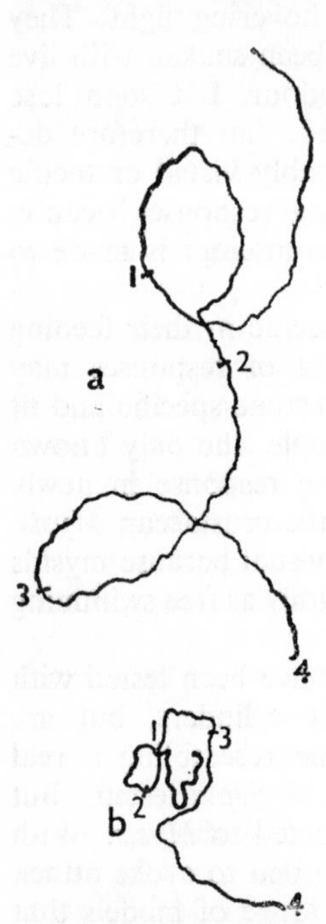

Figure 16. The tracks of a ladybird larva *Adalia*. (*a*) Before feeding and (*b*) after feeding on an aphid. (*After Banks.*)

It is remarkable that such apparently simple behaviour should enable larvae to find enough food to satisfy their needs, but ladybirds are such successful animals that there can be little doubt that it does.

4

Location of the Host by Parasites

Parasites, which depend upon their associations with other organisms for their food supply, must have some means of finding their hosts. Many endoparasites, such as the malaria parasite *Plasmodium*, which is transferred from one host to another by the Anopheles mosquito, are carried by animal vectors and play an almost passive role in this process. Generally these endoparasites are relatively inactive behaviourally and, concomitantly, some, such as tapeworms, have poorly developed nervous systems and sense organs. Nevertheless, they are not entirely inert and even the tapeworm *Taenia saginata* is capable of reacting to tactile stimuli and contracts to about a third of its original length if it is touched. Some nematodes perform complex activity rhythms inside their hosts. For example, microfilaria larvae of the nematode *Wuchereria bancrofti*, which in the adult stage causes elephantiasis in man, become active in the blood of their victims at night. During the day microfilariae are rarely found in the blood of an infected person, but at night the numbers increase and there may be as many as 40–50 millions in the circulatory system. This behaviour increases the nematode's chances of being picked up by its blood-sucking vector the mosquito, *Culex fatigans*, which is nocturnal in habit.

However, ectoparasites usually find their hosts for themselves, whether for the purpose of feeding or for laying eggs on them, and, in doing so, often perform complex behaviour.

Host recognition

Many parasites only associate with one or a limited number of hosts, which they must, of course, be capable of recognising and distinguishing from related organisms. However, like free-living animals with specific feeding requirements, they will only respond to suitable hosts because some of the releasing stimuli needed to evoke responses are highly specific and fit features of their hosts very closely. For example, egg-laying behaviour of the burr-seed fly *Euarestea inequalis* is restricted to one host because it is released by tactile stimulation from the tiny hooked spines on the fruits of the burweed *Xanthium*. The importance of these spines has been demonstrated experimentally. Flies will lay eggs on artificial burrs, studded to with small hooked pins to simulate spines, but will not oviposit on real burrs that have been despined.

Female Cabbage White butterflies *Pieris brassica*, searching for suitable oviposition sites, are attracted to leaves by visual stimuli. These have been investigated in the laboratory by testing butterflies to coloured cards. The females give a drumming reaction, consisting of quick alternating movements of the forelegs, before laying eggs which can be elicited by cards in the green to bluish-green range. Red, yellow, violet and blue cards, which, incidentally, elicit a feeding response, or cards in a series of shades of grey are ineffective. However, these butterflies are selective in their choice of a host plant and must therefore be responding to more than the colour of the leaves. They probably recognise suitable plants by their scent, which is a common means of identifying the host. Several leeches recognise their host in this way, which can be seen from their behaviour towards glass rods coated with host substances. They are not attracted by clean glass rods but attach themselves to rods that have been in contact with their hosts and attempt to suck from them. One, the medical leech *Hirudo*, will attach itself to a rod held beneath a man's armpit, and another, the duck leech *Theromyzon*, reacts in this way to a rod which has been in contact with the preen gland of a duck.

However, the host is often recognised by several of its characteristics and thermal stimuli also seem to be important identification stimuli to leeches that parasitise warm-blooded vertebrates. Both *Hirudo* and *Theromyzon* attach themselves to objects at about the body temperature of their hosts but ignore objects at other temperatures.

The female ichneumon fly *Nemeristis canescens* recognises caterpillars of the flour moth *Ephestia kuhniella*, in which she deposits her eggs, by their odour and can detect them at a range of 800 m. When females were tested in a Y-tube olfactometer (Figure 17) in which air laden with the odour of *Ephestia* larvae passes down one arm and uncontaminated air down the other, they were attracted to the smell of the host and 85% of them collected in that arm. However, the odours of related moth larvae, such as those of the wax moth *Melliphora grisella*, had no attraction for them in the apparatus. This is surprising because the larval ichneumons can be reared successfully on *Melliphora*, if it is artificially infected with them. But, ichneumons reared on *Melliphora* are attracted to this host as adults. Apparently they become conditioned to the new host during their development and, when they were tested in an olfactometer, about 66% were attracted to its odour. Nevertheless they still retain their inherent response for *Ephestia* and when they were given a choice between the smell of the natural host and that of the unnatural host in an olfactometer, 65·8% still prefered the odour of *Ephestia*.

Sequential arrangement of responses

However, the responses of parasites to their hosts are rarely, if ever, simple acts. Unfortunately analyses of their behaviour have mostly been incomplete but, at least, some parasites perform a succession of responses when they encounter their hosts. These are sometimes elicited by different stimuli from the host and, like many other instinctive activities, are arranged in the familiar stimulus-response chains.

The feeding behaviour of newly-hatched larvae of the

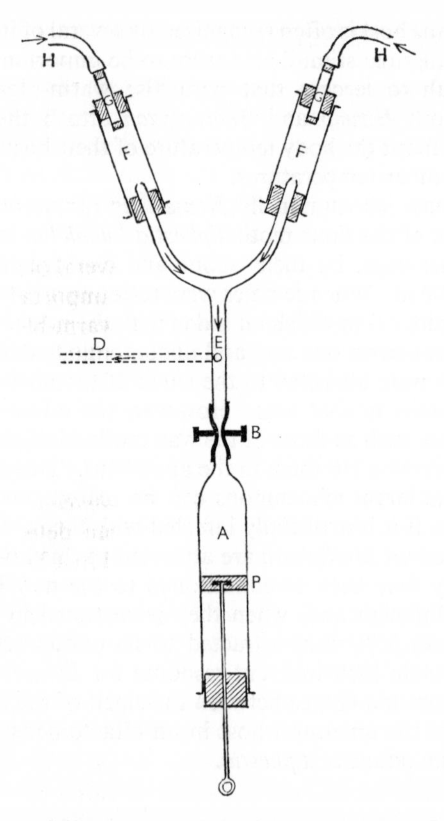

Figure 17. An olfactometer. A current of air (indicated by arrows) is drawn through the apparatus by a filter pump connected to D. Organisms can be housed in either of the tubes G so that air entering E from one side will be laden with their scent. The animals that are to be tested to the scent are placed in A. When they move along the apparatus they must choose between the scented and unscented channels at the Y-junction. Depending on their choice, they are subsequently trapped in one of the tubes F. The plunger P can be used to reduce the area of A until all animals have left it. (*After Thorpe and Jones.*)

corn-borer *Ostinia nubilalis* is certainly organised in this way. The larvae go through the following sequence: first, they find their way to suitable sites on the host plant, then, having done this they start to feed and, finally, if the food is suitable, feeding is maintained. Young larvae crawl from the leaves on which they hatch to less exposed parts of the plant, such as the confined spaces between the stem and leaves and in the ear husks. These places are dark and, in locating them, the larvae are probably reacting negatively to light. In fact, there is experimental evidence to support this because larvae on artificial plants, kept in sunlight, crawled to parts of the plants which were not exposed to the light. However, some other orientation response, possibly a thigmokinesis, in which larvae crawl into places where there is maximum bodily contact with other surfaces (see page 54) must be involved because about a third of them still found their way to the confined places on artificial plants which were kept in total darkness. The second response in the sequence, the initiation of feeding, is elicited by tactile stimulation and borers will bite almost anything that is rough and moist. However, they will only continue to feed if the correct chemical stimuli are received from the bitten material. Sugars are important and, if these carbohydrates are present, feeding is maintained.

There is a similar sequential arrangement of feeding responses in blood-sucking arthropods. Mosquitoes, for example, go through the sequence: locating the host from a distance, alighting on it, piercing the skin with the mouth-parts and, finally, sucking blood from it. The nature of the stimuli that elicit each of the responses is not known for certain, but the mosquito probably locates and orientates to its host partly by sight and also by detecting volatile chemicals emanating from it. Alightment may be in response to moisture and warmth from the host and piercing and biting are probably released by chemical stimulants.

The sheep tick *Ixodes ricinus* also performs elaborate behaviour when searching for its host. First, the hungry ticks orientate themselves to light and gravity by responses known as taxes (see Chapter 5) in a manner that is likely to bring them in contact with the host. They crawl towards the light and, consequently, crawl from their hiding places among vegetation to more exposed places. At the same time they react negatively to gravity. In the laboratory this behaviour was investigated by placing individuals on glass rods under controlled conditions of humidity and temperature. Usually they climbed up to the top of the rods and often descended for a limited distance but re-ascended and came to rest near the top. Under natural conditions individuals that behave in this way presumably crawl to the tips of plants, which are likely to brush against passing sheep. A stimulus, such as a shadow or vibration, which is likely to signal the approach of the host, elicits questing behaviour in the tick; the fore-part of the body is raised and the forelegs beat the air. If contact is made with the host, *Ixodes* then attaches itself. But, first the correct chemical and thermal stimuli must be received from it. Thus, ticks will attach themselves to tubes, covered with sheep's wool, at a temperature of 37°C, but similar tubes at lower temperatures or without the covering of wool, are not attractive.

It is surprising that the behaviour of many parasites has received such little attention, because, apart from their biological interest, many of them are vectors of important diseases or do harm to our crops. The relative ease with which some of them, such as ticks and leeches, can be attracted to inanimate objects coated with host substances or others, such as burr flies, can be discouraged from laying eggs on the host, suggests that a knowledge of their behaviour may be valuable in devising ways of controlling the economically important ones. Perhaps by the use of baited traps or by rendering the host unattractive in some way? But the potentialities of this kind of pest control have never been fully explored.

5

Movements

Animal movements can be divided into basically two kinds. First, there are the long distance journeys called migrations, which take animals from one locality to another and, second, the so-called localised or trivial movements, which tend to confine animals to the same habitat.

Localised movements are frequently simple orientation responses which seem to involve little more than adjustments of posture and locomotion to sensory stimuli. Several examples have already been given in previous chapters. For instance, planarian worms respond to substances emanating from food by orientating themselves towards it and by moving in the appropriate direction they are able to home on it (see page 35). Similarly, male mosquitoes, *Aedes aeggpti*, fly towards the source of vibrations caused by the beating wings of the female. They are almost certainly reacting to this stimulus because they are also attracted to vibrations from a tuning fork, as long as these are within a suitable frequency range.

Orientated movements of this kind, in which the animal moves in a fixed direction to the source of stimulation, are known as taxes. They occur to a variety of stimuli in different invertebrates, including gravity, water currents and light, as well as chemicals and vibrations.

Apart from their value in finding food and mates, taxes are important responses because they often guide animals to places where conditions are suitable for their survival. For example, young larvae of the European corn-borer respond to light by moving away from it and collect in dark places on their host plants (see page 45). Similarly, larvae of the blowfly

Eristalsis orientate themselves so that they move away from a source of illumination. Under natural conditions, this behaviour also enables them to collect in dark places, where they are inconspicuous and, therefore, less susceptible to attack from predators.

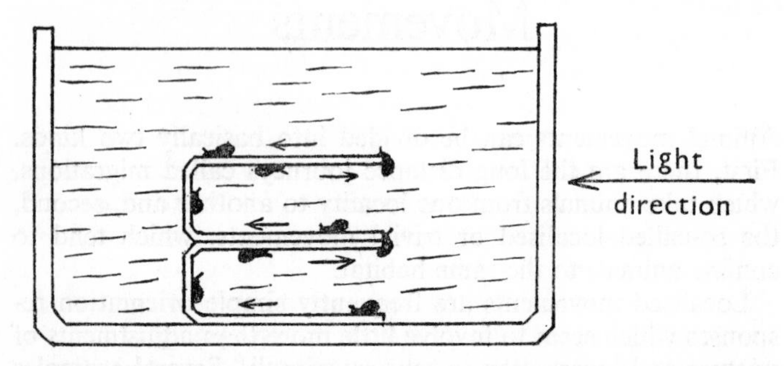

Figure 18. The behaviour of the periwinkle *Littorina neritoides* to light and gravity. Normally it reacts to light by a negative taxis, but when it is upside-down it becomes photopositive; it reacts to gravity by a negative taxis. As a result of these reactions it climbs progressively upwards in this experimental situation. (*After Fraenkel.*)

The importance of taxes in the lives of some littoral animals

Sometimes apparently complex behaviour has been analysed in terms of constituent taxes. The homing behaviour of the tiny periwinkle *Littorina neritoides* is a case in point. This animal is usually found in rock crevices above the high water mark on European shores. It orientates to gravity by a negative taxis and, therefore, climbs upwards if it is placed on a vertical surface. But its reactions to light are complex. Normally the periwinkle crawls away from the light, but when it is upside-down and under water it is photopositive (Figure 18). It has been suggested that these reactions guide an animal that has been dislodged back to its normal position on the shore. On a smooth, vertical rock face a dislodged periwinkle will climb upwards towards the high water mark. However, on its way, it is likely to encounter horizontal clefts in the rock, which might be expected to bar its upward progress. These are probably negotiated successfully because the periwinkle's photonegative behaviour takes it into the cleft along the floor, but the reversal of this response, when it climbs upside-down on to the roof, brings it out again.

Unfortunately taxes have usually been studied under controlled laboratory conditions and, although in cases such as that of *Littorina neritoides*, it is possible to guess at the value of the behaviour to the animal, the interpretations need to be confirmed by field observations. Nevertheless, in some investigations the functional importance of taxes has been established beyond reasonable doubt by studying them in the field and in the laboratory. For example, Professor G. E. Newell has shown that another common periwinkle, the edible one *Littorina littorea*, maintains its position on the sea shore by orientating to the sun's rays. Unlike its relative *Littorina neritoides*, this species is common on the middle shore of many beaches and, by marking individuals with dabs of brightly coloured paint, it is possible to show that they remain in approximately the same place for many weeks. This is not a result of inactivity because these periwinkles make regular feeding excursions. However, on their journeys they trace paths which bring them back to the starting point; they set off in one direction and then reverse the direction of movement, roughly countermarching the original track (Figure 19). During a field study of these animals on a muddy beach it was noticed that nearly all of the tracks left by periwinkles were either towards or away from the sun, which in itself suggests that they are orientating to the sun's rays. Subsequently the importance of the sun was demonstrated experimentally by showing that individuals on feeding excursions could be made to turn round and travel in the reverse direction by shading them from the sun and then reflecting its rays on to them from the opposite side with a mirror. Then, in a laboratory investigation, it was shown that these periwinkles orientate to an artificial light source in a manner that will account for the characteristic path traced by individuals orientating to the sun. At first they are photopositive and crawl towards the light, but after about 15 to 20 minutes they become photo-negative, turn round and move in the opposite direction.

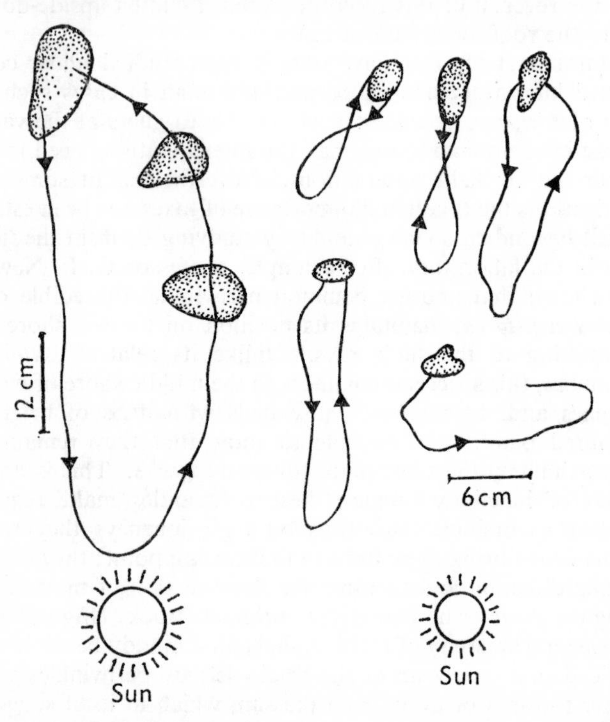

Figure 19. Tracks made by periwinkles *Littorina littorea* crawling on the sand near mid-tide level in bright sunshine. (*After Newell.*)

Sandhoppers *Talitrus saltator* also orientate to the sun and, by doing so, are able to return to their usual zone on the sea shore if they are moved from it. Individuals taken from the damp sand, in which they live, to dry sand higher up the beach, travel seawards until they reach favourable conditions. It can be shown that they too are orientating to the sun because their direction of movement can be altered at will by reflecting sunlight on to them from different angles with a mirror. But orientation must be a complex process because, unlike most taxes, which are in a constant direction to the source of stimulation (usually towards or away from it), the angle of orientation with the sun alters continuously as the sun's azimuth changes. To take a simplified example: sandhoppers living on a west-facing shore will need to orientate at an angle of about 180° to the sun when it rises at dawn, in order to travel seawards, by noon the angle will have altered to about 90° and at sunset it will be approximately 0°.

Clearly, sandhoppers must be able to compensate for movements of the sun and the most likely explanation is that they have a time-keeping mechanism which enables them to react appropriately to it at any given time. Indeed, the existence of some kind of internal clock has been established in *Talitrus* by transporting individuals from Pisa in Italy to Rossario in Argentina and showing that they still kept time with the position of the sun at Pisa and orientated to it as if they were there. Thus on one occasion transported sandhoppers orientated to the sun at an angle of 38° 30′ when they were tested at Rossario. But, although this angle was appropriate for the equivalent time at Pisa and would have taken the animals in a westerly, seaward direction, the sun was, of course, in a different position at Rossario and the sandhoppers travelled in an easterly direction.

Kineses

Animals sometimes respond to stimuli without moving in a fixed direction relative to their source. In these types of movements, which are known as kineses (singular: kinesis), the stimulus merely affects the activity of the animal. For example, it may affect the speed of movement (orthokinesis) or the frequency at which the animal turns and changes direction when it is moving (klinokinesis).

Kineses elicited by changes in the humidity of the surrounding air are an important component of the behaviour of woodlice. Orthokinesis has been demonstrated by observing in-

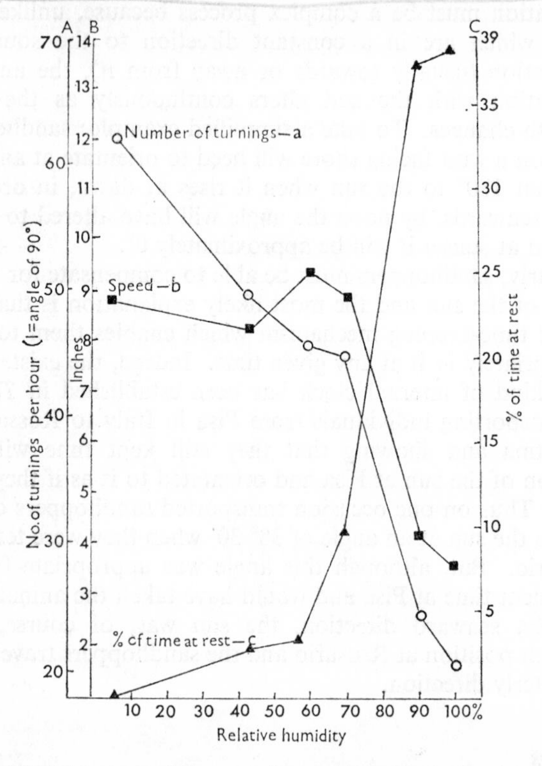

Figure 20. Behaviour of the woodlouse *Porcellio scaber* in constant humidities, calculated from an average of 30 individuals. The number of turnings (*a*) and speed of movement (*b*) both decrease with increasing humidity, while the percentage of time spent at rest (*c*) increases. (*After Waloff.*)

dividuals under conditions of fixed humidity and it has been shown that there is a relationship between the rate at which individuals move and the dampness of the air. Woodlice move rapidly and rest infrequently in dry air but, in progressively more humid air, they become less and less active (Figure 20). They also react klinokinetically to these changes: movement is in roughly straight lines in damp air but, in drier air, individuals change their direction of movement more and more frequently and, consequently, trace increasingly erratic paths.

Kineses are important responses because, like many taxes, they tend to confine movements to places in which conditions are suitable for their survival. For example, they tend to restrict woodlice to damp places where water loss through their

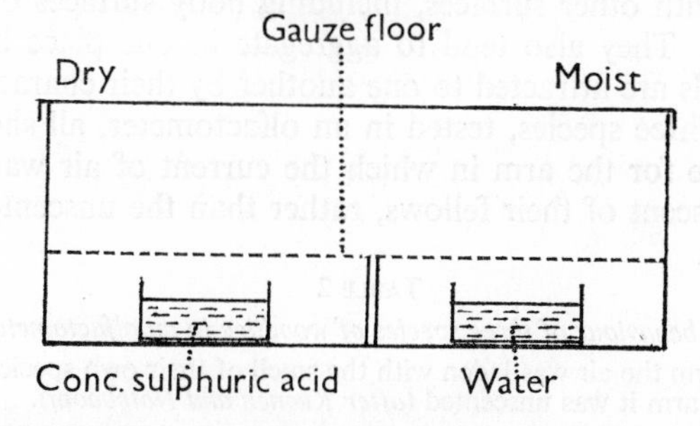

Figure 21. A choice chamber in which the air in one half is damp and the other dry.

permeable cuticles is minimised. The effectiveness of orthokinesis can be seen from the behaviour of woodlice in a choice chamber in which the air in one half is humid but in the other half is dry (Figure 21). Individuals tend to collect in those parts of the chamber where their rate of movement is least. This is, of course, on the damp side where they move slowly or come to rest. On the dry side, woodlice move rapidly and remain there for a relatively short time. Klinokinesis probably reinforces this effect. An individual that crosses the boundary from the damp to the dry side starts to change direction frequently and there is a good chance that its erratic movement will take it back into the favourable half of the chamber.

Under natural conditions woodlice certainly collect in damp places and presumably rely largely on these kinetic responses.

However, successful aggregation is not entirely dependent upon humidity reactions. Light, contact and chemical responses are all important. Woodlice orientate by a taxis to light and, because they are usually photonegative, they tend to collect in dark places which are also likely to be damp. But they do not merely settle in such places, they actually bunch together against one another which presumably reduces the rate at which water is lost by evaporation. This behaviour depends upon a contact response or thigmokinesis. Individuals tend to stop moving when a large proportion of the body is in contact with other surfaces, including body surfaces of other woodlice. They also tend to aggregate in one place because individuals are attracted to one another by their characteristic odour. Three species, tested in an olfactometer, all showed a preference for the arm in which the current of air was laden with the scent of their fellows, rather than the unscented arm (Table 2).

TABLE 2

The behaviour of three species of woodlice in an olfactometer

In one arm the air was laden with the smell of their own species; in the alternative arm it was unscented (*after Kuenen and Noteboom*).

Species	*Numbers collecting in each arm*		*Per cent. collecting in the scented arm*
	Scented	*Unscented*	
Oniscus	148	69	68
Porcellio	101	62	62
Armadillidium	115	55	62

Although it is important that woodlice aggregate in damp places, it is also necessary for them to move to new hiding places from time to time. Apart from the need to disperse in order to feed and breed, it is necessary to move if local conditions change and become unsuitable for survival. Not surprisingly, therefore, at least some of the orientation responses of woodlice become modified in unfavourable circumstances. Some species become photopositive in dry air so that they tend to crawl out of dark places into the light and others react in the same way if the temperature rises too much. Similarly the thigmokinetic response is modified by changes in humidity. In one investigation it was shown that individuals spent 92·6% of their time at rest against the sides of the glass vessel containing them when the relative humidity was 90–95% but they spent only 79·5% of the time behaving in this way when the relative humidity was reduced to 50–55%.

It is even necessary for woodlice to make occasional excursions from permanently damp habitats. This is because water is actually absorbed from saturated air and an excess may be accumulated in the body. They are unable to get rid of this excess by physiological means and, in order to lose it, woodlice must temporarily leave their hiding places and crawl into dry air, where water can be lost by evaporation. There is sometimes, therefore, a reversal of the normal humidity responses in saturated conditions. Individuals become increasingly active in damp air and, as a result, tend to collect in dry places. Presumably, when enough water has been lost, their behaviour reverts to normal and they move back into damp habitats.

This behaviour undoubtedly illustrates the way in which a combination of simple orientation responses can be of considerable survival value to an organism. But the behaviour of woodlice is by no means properly understood. Information is needed about the sense organs that detect changes in humidity and temperature. The need for more details about their ecology is, perhaps, even more pressing because the full significance of the orientation responses of woodlice and other animals, for that matter, can never be fully appreciated without a knowledge of their habits in natural surroundings.

Migrations

Most invertebrates spend the majority of their lives confined to one particular habitat or locality but, from time to time, some of them make long distance journeys from one place to another. Unfortunately there are only a few cases in which movements of this kind are as well documented as those of vertebrates. This is presumably because migrating invertebrates normally travel in small numbers and only one or two, such as locusts and some butterflies, move in large, conspicuous swarms. Nevertheless, it is possible to get an overall picture of the movements of animals by carefully recording the directions in which many individuals are travelling and, from data of this sort, it has been established that several insects do, in fact, migrate. For example, records of the Silver-Y moth *Plusia gamma* in Britain between 1933 and 1937 have shown that it makes an annual migration northwards in summer and then moves south after the middle of August.

Migratory movements can be distinguished from other kinds of locomotion in several ways, although there is unlikely to be a sharp dividing line between the two. First, migrations tend to lead animals to new localities, whereas localised movements tend to confine them to their habitats. Sometimes the distances travelled by invertebrate migrants are enormous and they rival those of birds. For example, there is evidence that the Painted Lady butterfly, *Vanessa cardui*, which journeys from North Africa to Europe, sometimes travels as far as 2,000 miles. Second, migratory movement has been aptly described as 'straightened out'. That is to say, it is persistently orientated in a particular direction and often barriers, such as mountain ranges, fail to interrupt movement in the correct direction. Thus the Long-tailed Blue butterfly, *Lampides boeticus*, has been recorded migrating at 12,000 ft. over the Himalayas and several insects are known to cross the Pyrenees on migratory flights. Finally, during migration there is a temporary inhibition of activities, which might hinder movement. For example, responses such as feeding, mating, oviposition, basking and cleansing all fail to be elicited by appropriate stimulation in the Great Southern White butterfly, *Ascia monuste*, when it is migrating.

Some migrations are two-way movements, so that an individual that journeys in one direction will subsequently make the return journey in the reverse direction. Birds, which travel to and from breeding and feeding grounds, undoubtedly migrate in this way, but invertebrates generally have shorter lives and there is less evidence for migrations involving return journeys. Nevertheless, some butterflies and moths do seem to make two-way migrations. For example flight records of Red Admiral butterflies, *Vanessa atalanta*, have shown that they travel north during the summer in Britain but, from September onwards, the direction of movement is predominantly south. Similarly, in Alabama, the Yellow butterfly *Catopsilia eubule* migrates in a south-easterly direction from July to September and in the opposite direction in March and April. But, unlike bird migrations, the same individuals do not always travel in both directions. For example, Monarch butterflies, *Danaus plexippus*, whose summer breeding range extends over the entire United States and the southern parts of Canada, make an impressive migration southwards in September. At first they fly individually or in small groups, but then join up to form large swarms. Those migrating down the eastern states over-winter in Florida, where breeding also takes place. Subsequently, the offspring of the original migrants make the northerly migration to the summer range.

Examples of one-way migrations made by invertebrates, which never seem to involve a return journey, are much more common, particularly in the arthropods. Migrating locust swarms, for instance, do not usually return to their place of origin and aphids also make one-way journeys from one host plant to another. But, unlike locusts, aphids are only capable of feeble flight and, in the past, some authors have preferred to distinguish between passive aphid-like movements, which they called dispersals, and active migrations by strong fliers, such as locusts. However, this distinction leads to immediate difficulties and does not seem to be justified. It turns out that migrating locusts are often as dependent upon the wind as aphids. They too are frequently blown along so that the direction of movement and speed of a swarm is often related to that of the wind. Furthermore, it is wrong to suggest that the long-distance movements of aphids are entirely passive. They are undoubtedly blown by the wind, but take-off and landing on their journeys are active locomotory responses. Experimental studies have shown that before setting off there is a sharp rise in the aphids general locomotory activity, which is eventually triggered into flight. Individuals are then attracted by a positive taxis to the ultra-violet light from the sky and fly upwards until they are transported passively along in air currents. Eventually there is a change in the response to light and then the aphids are attracted to light of the shorter wave part of the spectrum so that they fly downwards to the foliage beneath them. However, they are probably incapable of recognising their specific host plants from the air and make several alightments before the correct host is discovered.

The importance of migrations

Two-way migrations of vertebrates often enable them to avoid difficult conditions which occur in an otherwise suitable locality, and allow them to return when conditions become favourable again. Many migrant birds, for example, spend each summer in Britain, where they breed, but migrate before winter commences and food becomes scarce. Two-way migrations of invertebrates seem to have a similar function. Monarch butterflies avoid the cold winters of Canada and the northern United States, which they are incapable of surviving, by migrating south. But climatic factors are not always the important ones. The Japanese polychaete worm *Tylorrhynchus heterochaetus* which is able to live in fresh-water habitats such as paddy fields and the filter beds of water-works, migrates to the lower reaches of estuaries in order to breed. This is necessary for the survival of the larvae, which cannot osmoregulate successfully in fresh-water. When the young worms have developed this ability, they are carried on flood tides to fresh-water habitats.

However, the biological significance of migrations which do not involve a return journey has often been in dispute. One suggestion is that they act as a safety valve, being a way of getting rid of excess population. But, if this is so, migration would be a lethal character and it is difficult to see how it could have been selected during the process of evolution. A more acceptable hypothesis is that, by moving from place to place, animals are able to colonise new habitats and, thereby, keep pace with the location of suitable habitats, especially new ones when they occur. This is a difficult hypothesis to test,

TABLE 3

A comparison of the habitat ratings and aeronautical habit in spiders

The habitats are rated on a numerical scale, based on relative permanence, varying from woods, heather and other permanent places (+2) to impermanent habitats, such as straw and detritus (−2) (*after Southwood*).

Habit	*Total number of species living in each habitat rating*					*Total score*	*Mean score*
	+2	+1	0	−1	−2		
Migrant (aeronaut)	1	8	5	1	3	+3	+0·16
Non-migrant (non-aeronaut)	13	8	4	1	0	+33	+1·27

but there is a good deal of indirect evidence to support it. If it is correct, one would expect to find a higher level of migratory activity in animals associated with temporary habitats than those living in more stable ones, because the need to move is greater. Just such a relationship has been shown to exist in several groups of arthropods. For example, none of the British dragonflies that inhabit permanent places, such as rivers and streams, migrate, but 8 out of 11 species living in less permanent ponds and gravel pits are either regular or occasional migrants. Similarly, most of the British Macrolepidoptera that have a migratory habit live on annuals or plants with relatively short life histories whereas the non-migrants tend to live on more permanent plants, such as trees and large bushes.

There is a similar relationship between the tendency to migrate and impermanence of habitat in araneid spiders. These animals migrate by crawling to the tips of vegetation and squeezing out a droplet of silk, which is caught by the wind and pulled into a strand. When the pull becomes strong enough the spider is carried away by the wind. Individuals may travel for long distances and reach great heights and one spider was even recorded at a height of 15,000 ft over Louisiana. The normal habitats of these spiders have been assessed by giving each an arbitrary score based on its relative permanence, and it can be seen from the data in Table 3 that the migratory species tend to live in less permanent habitats than their non-migrant relatives.

Timing of migrations

Migrations of many of the animals that make two-way journeys are seasonal. Usually they occur in spring and autumn, and are probably triggered by climatic factors which occur at these times of year. But the timing of one-way migrations is normally less predictable and often seems to depend upon local factors in the habitat. Some of these migrations are triggered by factors that herald the approach of unsatisfactory conditions. For example, crowding on the host initiates it in the aphid *Megoura viciae*. Aphids are polymorphic and, when crowding occurs, wingless females give birth to the winged migrant forms. The effect of high population densities can be demonstrated without maintaining the aphids on plants. In one investigation these conditions were simulated by confining individuals in specimen tubes crowded with several other aphids. After this treatment, females, whose previous offspring had been wingless, gave birth to a proportion of winged individuals in the next and subsequent batches of young. Controls, which received exactly the same treatment, except that they were isolated in their specimen tubes, did not produce any winged progeny throughout the experiment.

Wing polymorphism is common in other insects, including many beetles. For example, populations of the weevil *Sitona hispidula* frequently consist of two forms, one of which is a known migrant and has fully developed wings and the other a non-migrant, with vestigial wings. It might be expected that the relative abundance of the two forms in this and other animals would be geared by natural selection to the relative permanence of the habitat. The more permanent the habitat the higher the proportion of non-migrants and *vice versa*. But much more data, including more observations of the migrations of these animals and the conditions under which they live, are needed before conclusions of this kind are justified.

6

Escape Responses

Almost all invertebrates are preyed upon by a variety of other animals and, not surprisingly therefore, most of them seem to have some way of defending themselves from attack by predators. Several, such as some species of woodlice, which roll themselves into a ball, escape by becoming static and, as a result, may avoid detection altogether. But many others make active escapes and some will actually face up to and fight their enemies. Normally these animals are endowed with some way of inflicting damage. For example, the shore crab *Carcinus maenas* will defend itself with its claws. This crab often displays when it is about to be attacked by raising the anterior part of the body, holding its claws in front of it and bracing its outstretched legs. If the attacker is not deterred by the display and approaches, *Carcinus* may strike at it with its claws and, if the crab is caught and held, it will attempt to free itself by biting with its claws and pushing out its legs.

Bluff displays and camouflage

However, animals with offensive weapons are by no means the only ones to display to their enemies. Several insects also display when they are startled, but unlike crabs they have no way of causing damage to the attacker. The display is, therefore, a bluff and is only successful if the predator is alarmed by it and, thereby, deterred from attacking. The bodies of insects that behave in this way are often adorned with bright colours and in some beetles, mantids and several of the Lepidoptera, these colours are arranged in circular patterns which have an unmistakable resemblance to the shape of a vertebrate eye and probably help to frighten the attacker. Each wing of the peacock butterfly *Nymphalis io* bears one of these eye spots. When it is startled the wings are depressed and elevated, protracted and retracted in a complex series of movements which display the eye spots prominently.

This behaviour has protective value against at least one predator because yellow buntings often avoid displaying peacock butterflies. There is experimental evidence that the eye-spots play an important role in discouraging attacks from the buntings because, although butterflies whose eye-spots have been removed still display, they are attacked more frequently by the birds. Equal numbers of intact butterflies and butterflies with eye-spots removed were introduced into the cages of six yellow buntings, but whereas displays from butterflies with eye-spots elicited 149 startle responses, those without eye-spots were successful on only 37 occasions.

Further evidence of the effectiveness of eye-like patterns in releasing escape responses was obtained by testing the reaction of yellow buntings to a series of patterns suddenly shown to them when they were feeding. The patterns were shown in pairs. In each experiment one of them was more eye-like than the other and this always elicited more escape responses. Thus, a circle was more effective than a cross and a series of concentric rings, shaded to give a three dimensional eye-like effect, startled the birds more often than a series of rings in a flat, unshaded pattern (Figure 22).

But, apart from their value as a deterrent to would-be attackers, eye-spots may have a second function. It has been suggested that predators, which are not startled by the display, direct their attacks at them. This would enhance the animal's chance of escape because eye-spots are usually situated in relatively non-vulnerable places, such as the edges of the wings of many butterflies. Occasional observations, such as one of a lizard picking out the eye-spot of a small heath and allowing it to escape, support this hypothesis, but it is difficult to test experimentally. There is some evidence that yellow buntings direct their attacks at prominent features of the prey because, in one series of experiments, they tended to attack meal-worms on parts of the body that had been adorned with black spots. But it does not necessarily follow that they react to natural eye-spots in this way.

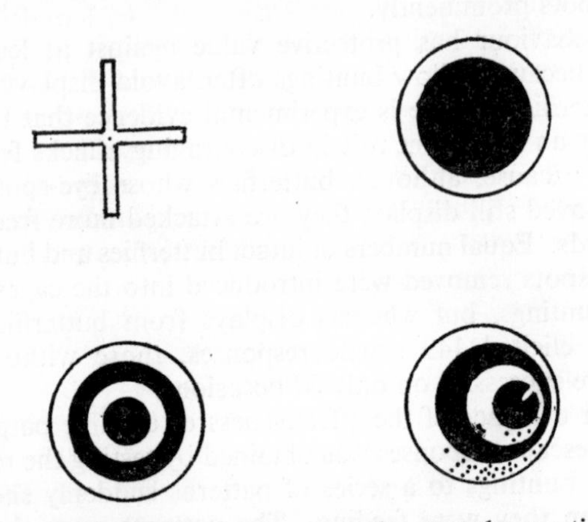

Figure 22. Four of the patterns used to test the reactions of chaffinches to eye-like shapes. (*After Blest.*)

The bluff display of the praying mantis is usually a secondary protective mechanism because the animal is often so well camouflaged that it frequently escapes detection altogether; a display would draw unnecessary attention to itself. For example, the mantis *Acanthops falcata* is camouflaged by its remarkable appearance to dried, shrivelled leaves. Male *Acanthops* rarely display, but females sometimes react to predators in this way. When the female does display she looks very different from her usual appearance. She sways and sidles, raises the black and yellow wings and tegmina and exposes the red and black part of her abdomen to the predator. This act is certainly successful in deterring some of her enemies because snakes and lizards, which will normally feed on mantids, have never been observed to attack one that is displaying.

But, unlike mantids, most animals that depend upon camouflage to escape detection do not display to their predators. Most of them become static when they are likely to be attacked. Thus, during daylight, stick caterpillars of geometrid moths, which are camouflaged to resemble twigs, increase their likeness by holding on to a branch with the posterior claspers and assuming a twig-like attitude. These caterpillars are similar to twigs in coloration and shape, even to such detail as humps on the body which resemble buds and leaf scars. Different species are camouflaged to resemble their specific food plants. *Ennomos aliniaria*, which feeds on birch, has a slender body and relatively smooth surface so that it looks like a birch twig and *Ennomos quercinaria*, which feeds on oak, has the rougher and stockier appearance of an oak twig.

The effectiveness of the camouflage has been tested experimentally by offering freshly killed geometrid caterpillars together with real twigs of a similar size to captive jays and chaffinches. Unfortunately live caterpillars could not be used because, surprisingly, they moved under the experimental conditions and were thereby recognised as food by the birds. Nevertheless, this is an interesting observation because it shows that the caterpillars must remain static for the camouflage to be effective. In the experiments, the birds usually ignored both the dead caterpillars and the twigs, but occasional chance encounters did occur so that caterpillars were sometimes eaten. As a result of these accidental discoveries, some of the jays were able to learn to recognise the caterpillars and to distinguish them from twigs. However, jays are unusually perceptive birds and chaffinches could not do this. After feeding on a caterpillar, a chaffinch would peck indiscriminately at all twig-like objects, but was soon discouraged if only real twigs were found.

Rapid responses

In contrast to the escape behaviour of geometrid caterpillars, many invertebrates depend upon speed of reaction to avoid their enemies. For example, tubiculous worms, such as the group of Sabellid polychaetes known as fanworms, which extend a crown of tentacles from the end of a protective tube, rapidly withdraw exposed parts whenever danger threatens. This response is extremely sensitive to stimuli that are likely to be associated with predators, such as shadows, and, in the laboratory, the fanworm *Branchiomma vesiculosum* will react to a stimulus that involves a decrease in illumination of only 0·003 metre/candles. However, unnecessary responses are kept to a minimum and individuals do not react at all to stimuli, such as sudden increases in illumination, which are not normally caused by predators.

The rapidity of withdrawal in these worms is due partly to the speed of contraction of the longitudinal muscles of the body wall, which effect the response. But there is also a minimal delay between receipt of the stimulus by the sensory receptors and the arrival of the ensuing nerve impulses at the muscles. This is because the impulses travel along special giant axons in the ventral nerve cord, which, by virtue of their large diameters, can conduct impulses extremely rapidly. In one fanworm *Myxicola infundibulum*, which has a particularly well developed withdrawal reflex, there are two giant axons in the first two segments, but these fuse to form one enormous axon, which occupies most of the nerve cord and runs for almost its entire length. It may have a diameter of up to 1·7 mm and is capable of transmitting impulses at velocities of between 3 and 20 m/sec. Thick branches of the giant axon leave the ventral nerve cord along segmental nerves and directly innervate the longitudinal muscles, so that impulses also travel rapidly on the motor side of the reflex.

The need to react rapidly in response to predators has resulted in the evolution of giant axons in completely different groups of animals. For example, they also occur in molluscs, such as the squid *Loligo*, which darts suddenly backwards when it is startled. The squid's response is an unusual one. Circular muscles in the wall of the mantle cavity, which is a respiratory chamber containing gills, rapidly contract, expelling a jet of water through the funnel of the cavity with enough force to propel the animal backwards. At the same time a cloud of ink, which is released from glands in the mantle cavity, provides cover for the squid's escape.

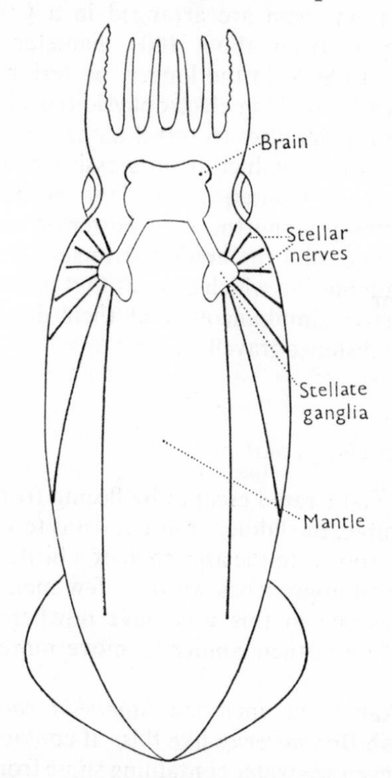

Figure 23. A diagram of part of the nervous system of the squid. The stellar nerves, which radiate from a pair of stellate ganglia, supply the circular muscles of the mantle. (*After Roberts.*)

The circular muscles of the mantle cavity wall are innervated by a series of nerves, radiating from a stellate ganglion (Figure 23). Each contains a single giant axon, through which the response is mediated. It is important that impulses travelling along these giant axons arrive simultaneously at the circular muscles because they must contact synchronously for a maximally efficient response. But this presents a problem because the stellar nerves are of different lengths. However, the giant axons in them are arranged in a graded series of thickness, varying from about 100μ diameter in the short, anterior nerves to 800μ in the longer, posterior nerves and it has been shown by making electrophysiological recordings of the time taken for impulses to travel along parts of the axons that the thick axons conduct at progressively faster velocities than thinner ones. Consequently giant axon impulses will travel more rapidly along the long posterior nerves than the short anterior ones and the graded arrangement of axons can be seen as an adaptation which ensures that impulses travelling along them arrive simultaneously at their destinations, irrespective of the distance travelled.

Escape by outpacing predators

Some animals make rapid escapes by fleeing from their predators. For example, the fiddler crab *Uca* runs to the entrance of its burrow in response to the approach of a bird and disappears into it if the bird approaches within a few metres. But many animals that escape in this way have nowhere to hide and simply depend upon their ability to move more rapidly than the attacker.

One remarkable sea anemone *Stomphia coccinea* escapes from the starfish *Dermasterias* like this. If contact is made with the starfish or even sea water containing slime from it, *Stomphia* detaches itself from the substratum and swims away. At first the anemone contracts, but 2–3 seconds later it elongates and then performs a series of whirling and side to side movements, which are a prelude to detachment. Swimming, which follows, involves undulating movements of the column, base and oral disc, but is inefficient, and the anemone travels relatively short distances. The longest observed journey was of only 80 cm, but even this would be adequate to take the animal well out of the range of a starfish.

Some limpets, such as *Acmaea limatula*, which escape from predators like crabs by clamping firmly down on the substratum, also flee from approaching starfish. When individuals of *Acmaea* are touched by the starfish *Pisaster ochraceus*, the shell is raised several metres above the foot and the limpet glides away, easily outpacing the assailant. This is an extremely sensitive response and it can be elicited if a single tube foot of a starfish is brought into contact with the shell margin of *Acmaea*. Other gastropods are equally sensitive and large ones, such as *Haliotis* and *Lottia*, will flee from tiny starfish which are incapable of harming them. At first sight this seems to be an absurd situation. But speed is an essential component of these escape responses and it is probably more important to react to any stimulus that might indicate the approach of a predator, than to wait and identify the attacker before responding.

7

Social Behaviour

The habits of the majority of invertebrates are essentially solitary and, apart from courtship and aggressive encounters, there is little or no contact between members of the same species. On the other hand, there is a relatively small group of insects, about six thousand out of a total of perhaps a million species, which live in beautifully organised societies. These insects are, in fact, restricted to only two orders: the Hymenoptera, which includes the bees, wasps and ants, and the Isoptera, the termites. Nevertheless, within this small group the elaboration of instinctive behaviour has reached a level which is unparalleled in any non-social invertebrates.

In contrast to the societies of vertebrates, these insect communities usually consist of the progeny of only one or a limited number of individuals. For example, in colonies of honeybees, *Apis mellifera*, and several other Hymenoptera there is normally only one fertile female, the queen. Most of the members of the colony are her offspring. There is a limited number of males, but the large majority of individuals are sterile females, which perform the menial tasks essential for the well-being of the community. A termite community has a slightly different composition; there is usually one pair of sexual reproductives, the king and queen, and sterile individuals of both sexes.

The nature of social aggregations

Unlike the majority of animals, social invertebrates are attracted to members of their own species even when they are not reproducing and, consequently, they tend to aggregate in groups. When about a hundred lightly anaesthetised worker honeybees are scattered in a small box they usually form a single cluster on recovering consciousness. There are probably several factors which attract them to one another. One of these is the scent produced by the abdominal scent glands, because bees are strongly attracted to it in a Y-tube olfactometer (Figure 17; page 44). In one experiment, 68 bees collected in the arm of the olfactometer, in which the current of air was drawn over recently excised abdominal glands, and only 16 in the alternative arm, in which the air was unscented. But scent is not the only attractive factor because scattered bees will aggregate around a closed metal cylinder in which live individuals are imprisoned. There is indirect evidence that they may react to vibrations from the enclosed bees or heat generating from their bodies. Bees will aggregate around an empty tin whose walls are made to vibrate mechanically and, if they are given a choice between two empty tins, differing in temperature by about 2°C, they collect around the warmer one as long as it is below 37°C.

Worker honeybees are also strongly attracted to their queen and there is little doubt that her presence is the main factor that holds a colony together. If she is removed the other members are usually prepared to fuse with another colony. It was found, for example, that a queenless group of honeybees placed in a hive, which communicated with another one by a vestibule, would move into the neighbouring colony if it contained either a mated or a virgin queen. Similarly, about 20 hours after removal of the queen from a colony of army ants *Eciton*, the workers will readily join a community which has a queen.

Division of labour and caste determination

But social life in these animals involves much more than a mere aggregation of a number of insects in the same place. Even in colonies of the primitive social wasp *Belonogaster*, in which all females are fertile, there is a well-marked division of labour. This is possible because females of different ages perform different duties; newly emerged *Belonogaster* females devote themselves to tending the brood, then they become foragers and, finally, older ones lay eggs. Workers in colonies

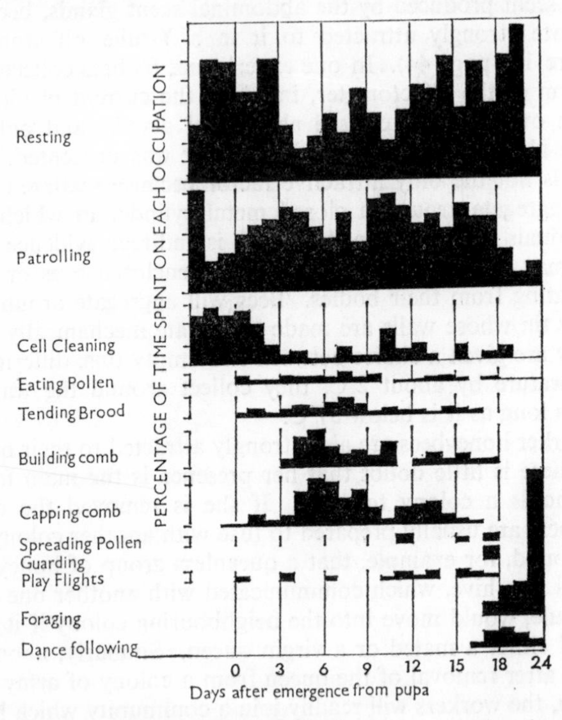

Figure 24. An analysis of the work done by a worker honeybee during her life. At any age one occupation tends to predominate but she may perform other tasks. (*After Lindauer*.)

of the more highly organised Hymenoptera carry out a similar sequence of tasks. In a society of ants, *Myrmica scabrinodis*, workers reared during the current season serve as brood nurses, those produced during the previous season act as nest builders and older ones leave the nest on foraging missions.

Similarly, ageing honeybees perform a succession of duties, although they do not adhere strictly to the schedule (Figure 24). At any age there is a tendency for one activity to predominate in their lives, but if other jobs in the hive need doing they may devote themselves to these.

Queens do not normally perform the same duties as workers. In fact, apart from egg-laying, they are relatively inactive. But, surprisingly, they have the same genetic constitution as workers. This can be demonstrated in a colony of honeybees by transferring an egg or a newly hatched larva from one of the special, sac-shaped cells in which queens develop to one of the cells for potential workers. A worker is usually reared from it, never a queen. Conversely, if an egg or larva is transferred from a worker to a queen cell it normally develops into a queen. It is almost certain that a larva's development is determined by its diet. Throughout the larval stage potential queens are fed on a protein-rich secretion, known as royal jelly, from the hypopharyngeal and mandibulary glands of adult workers, whereas larvae destined to become workers are only fed on this for the first three days.

Despite their genetic potentialities the vast majority of individuals become workers. Clearly there must be some control of the production of different castes and usually this seems to be through a system of chemical substances, known as pheromones, released by individuals in the community. One, which has been identified as 9-oxodec-2-enoic acid, is secreted by the mandibulary glands of the queen honeybee. It is picked up by the workers and passed from one to another throughout the colony (see below). It ensures that no rival queens will develop in the community by inhibiting the construction of queen cells by the workers. If the queen is removed, the workers no longer receive the queen substance and build queen cells.

The king and queen in a colony of European dry wood termites, *Kalotermes flavicollis*, also inhibit the development of other fertile individuals because, within 6 to 10 days of their removal, supplementary reproductives appear in the nest. One pair of these is allowed to survive by the other members of the community and it becomes the new royal couple. When she is present the queen produces an inhibitory pheromone which is given off with excrement through the anus. Consequently, if she is fixed in a solid screen between two otherwise queenless colonies, the production of supplementary reproductives is inhibited on the side containing her abdomen and not at all on the other side. Her inhibitory effect persists if the integumental glands of the abdomen are covered with varnish, so that these are not the source of the pheromone. However, if the queen's anus is blocked she no longer prevents the development of the supplementary reproductives.

Pheromones and feeding behaviour

The pheromone produced by the queen honeybee is probably distributed over her body when she cleans herself and then picked up by workers, which lick her. As a result, she only inhibits the construction of queen cells when the workers can reach her and, if she is suspended among them in a wire gauze cage through which they cannot push their probosces, queen's cells usually appear within forty-eight hours. However, to be effective the pheromone must spread rapidly through the entire colony and, as this may consist of many thousands of individuals, it is inconceivable that each one obtains its share from actual contact with her. The most likely explanation is that the pheromone is passed from one individual to another when regurgitated food is exchanged between them. Certainly food substances are distributed rapidly through a colony in this way. In one experiment, six worker bees, belonging to a colony of over 24,000, were allowed to collect a dose of sugar labelled with radioactive phosphorus. Five hours after their return to the hive, samples of the bees were examined and 25% were found to be radioactive and had, therefore, shared in the original sugar. A day later 50% had imbibed some of it.

A food-sharing encounter between two honeybees usually starts when one extends its proboscis and thrusts it towards the mouth parts of another individual. This may induce it to regurgitate a droplet of food from its stomach, which is then sucked up by the soliciting bee. An elaborate exchange of stimuli appears to take place between the two participants. Visual ones are undoubtedly involved, but they seem to be relatively unspecific because hungry bees will beg from excised heads of workers and also from crude models with wire antennae. Tactile stimuli are also exchanged and, after the removal of the antennae, which constantly make contact with those of the partner during a food-sharing bout, bees are able to offer food but unable to beg for it.

The antennae of the ants *Formica sanguinia* and *F. fusca* also move continuously when these animals share food with other individuals in their colonies. Both the antennae and the fore-legs are used to palpate the partner. But, unlike bees, removal of both antennae does not prevent ants from soliciting food, although they are less successful than usual in their attempts to do so.

Communication of a food source

Ants returning to the nest after successful foraging missions are able to communicate the location of their discoveries by laying scent trails. For example, when a worker of the fire ant *Solenopsis saevissima* finds a rich food source, such as a freshly killed mealworm or a sugar solution, it inspects its find and may feed from it. When the ant returns home it lays a trail of scent, which is secreted from Dufour's gland and released through the extruded sting. Most workers that stumble across the trail follow it in an outward direction, which leads them to the food. The first arrivals repeat the action of the discoverer and lay more trails on the homeward journey, thereby recruiting still more workers. However, the process of recruitment stops when there is over-crowding at the food. No new trails are laid because new recruits are unable to reach the food and turn back without secreting one and the trails already laid soon evaporate.

Honeybees have a more elaborate system of communicating

information which has been interpreted largely as a result of research by Professor K. von Frisch. The successful forager performs a complex dance in the hive. This excites some of the hive bees which follow the dancer, touching her with their

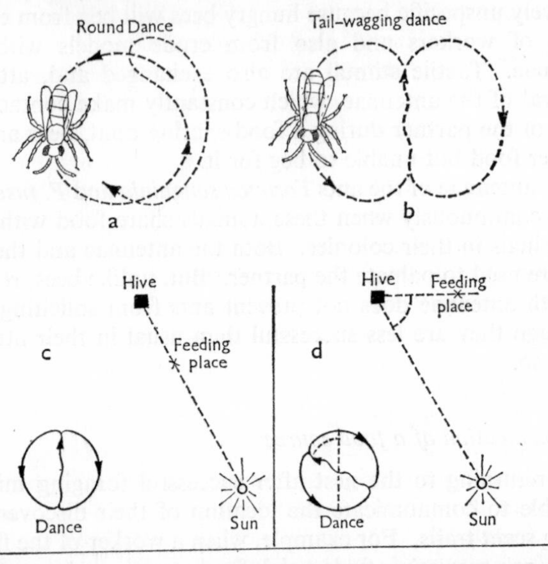

Figure 25. (*a*) The round dance and (*b*) the waggle dance of worker honeybees. (*c*) and (*d*): Communication of the direction of food during the waggle dance. The angle between the food source and the position of the sun is represented by the angle between the axis of the dance and the vertical. (*After Von Frisch and Lindauer.*)

antennae as they do so. The characteristic form of the dance conveys information to them about the discovery and, subsequently, they leave the nest and fly off in search of it.

The forager may, in fact, perform one of two dances on her return to the nest. If the discovery of, say, a new crop of flowers has been made within 80 m of the hive, she performs a 'round dance', moving in circles, first to one side and then to the other (Figure 25). This communicates relatively little information to the hive bees. It is merely a signal for them to go out to search for flowers which have the same odour as the scent adhering to the finder's body. However, if the food is at a greater distance, she performs a 'waggle-tail' dance, which is much more informative. As she dances, she traces out a figure-of-eight pattern and, during the straight run between the two loops of the eight, her whole body is waggled from side to side (Figure 25). The rhythm of this dance communicates the distance of the food to the hive bees. Foragers returning from relatively short distances make short and frequent waggle runs and those from further away make progressively longer and, therefore, less frequent runs. Thus a bee that has discovered food 100 m away makes about 60 waggle runs per minute, one whose discovery is 2,000 m. away 13 runs per minute and one returning from 4,000 m only 9 per minute.

It has been shown by taking audiospectrographic recordings that bees also produce a pulsed sound with a frequency of about 250 c/s during the waggle-run. The number of pulses is related to the distance of the food so that, if bees are sensitive to sounds of this kind, this may also convey distance information to them. Individuals returning from a food source 106 m from the hive make an average of between 5·4 and 10·2 pulses per waggle run, those from 700 m, between 30·8 and 43·6, and so on.

The waggle-tail dance even provides detailed information about the direction of the food and this is usually to within an accuracy of about 3°. The dance is normally performed on a vertical honeycomb and the angle between the sun and the food source is represented by the angle between the vertical and the tail-wagging run (Figure 25). Consequently, when food lies towards the sun, the waggle run is directly upwards and, when it is away from the sun, the run is downwards. If the food is at an angle to the sun then the run is performed at the appropriate angle to the vertical.

The quality and quantity of food is indicated by the duration and intensity of the dance. When food is rich and plentiful, the dance is performed vigorously and frequently, and many bees are recruited to search for it. But, when it is of poor quality or scant, the dance is weak and few are induced to forage.

There are interesting differences in the dances of European races of honeybees, each of which has its own 'dialect'. For instance, the waggle-tail dance of Italian honeybees *Apis mellifera lingustica* has a slower rhythm than that of Austrian bees *A. mellifera carnica*, and if individuals of these two races are artificially mixed in the same colony they misunderstand one another. An Austrian bee, which receives information from the dance of an Italian, of a food source 100 m away, overestimates the distance and flies 120 m. Conversely, Italian bees underestimate distances communicated to them by dancing Austrians; they fly only 80 m when the food is at a distance of 100 m.

As might be expected, interspecific differences between the dances of bees are greater than those between races. Our native honeybee *Apis mellifera* only occasionally dances on a horizontal surface outside the hive, but the Indian honeybee *A. florea* always does so and dances in the direction of the food so that there is no transposition of the angle between the sun and the food into one with the vertical plane. Stingless bees of the sub-family *Meliponini*, which are found in South America, are particularly interesting because successful foragers lay scent trails on vegetation and on the ground along the route to the food. On returning to the hive they run about excitedly, which attracts the attention of the hive bees. However, there is no communication of either the distance or the direction of the food. Nevertheless, recruits are guided to the food either by following the scent trails or by following other individuals to it.

It is interesting to speculate that the system of communication in the Meliponini may represent an intermediate stage in the evolution of the honeybees' dance from the trail-laying habit. Certainly much more information is required to justify a conclusion of this sort, but there is little doubt that the comparative study of behaviour in these and other animals is likely to provide evidence of the phylogenetic history of behaviour patterns, just as the study of comparative morphology has provided valuable information about the evolution of anatomical structures.

8

Habituation and Associative Learning

It is often assumed that invertebrates are endowed with a full repertoire of instinctive responses and learn little during their lives. But, although this is probably true of the large majority, there are undoubtedly exceptions. Some cephalopods, for instance, have such well-developed abilities to learn in the laboratory that it is difficult to imagine that learning does not play an important role in determining their behaviour under natural conditions. These animals are capable of associating previously unrelated stimuli or events. Octopuses, for example, which are shown an unfamiliar object on a number of occasions and are presented with food at the same time learn to associate the two and, as a result, attack the object whenever it appears (see below). However, associative learning is almost certainly a complex nervous process and it is unlikely that all invertebrates have the ability to learn in this way. Nevertheless, most of them seem to be capable of habituating to repeated stimulation, that is to say, they are able to learn to ignore innocuous stimuli that occur over and over again. Even some of the Protozoa can profit from their experience in this sense. For example, the ciliate *Vorticella nebulifera*, which lives attached to fresh-water plants or other solid objects by a retractile stalk habituates to sudden stimuli, such as vibrations. At first it reacts by contracting, but it becomes less responsive to successive stimulations and eventually fails to respond altogether.

Habituation of withdrawal and feeding responses

Escape responses of many animals habituate to repeated stimulation and, in the case of the ragworm *Nereis diversicolor*, this can be observed under natural conditions. These worms extend from their burrows in estuarine mud and feed at the surface. But they withdraw rapidly in response to almost any sudden stimulus, such as a shadow or nearby disturbance in the mud. However, if the same stimulus occurs repeatedly, they learn to ignore it and continue to feed whenever it occurs.

TABLE 4

The rates of habituation of ragworms, Nereis pelagica, *to different kinds of stimulation* (after Clark)

Stimulus (given at one-minute intervals)	*Trials necessary for habituation*	
	Substantial habituation	*Total habituation*
Mechanical shock combined with sudden decrease in light intensity	45+	65+
Sudden increase in light intensity	40	60+
Sudden decrease in light intensity	15	50
Moving shadow	4–5	15–20
Mechanical shock	2–10	12–35

In the laboratory several species of ragworms will inhabit glass tubes and, within them, carry out apparently normal activities such as periodically driving currents of water through their tubes with undulating movements of the body. They also withdraw in response to sudden changes in illumination, mechanical and tactile stimuli and, in the case of *Nereis pelagica,* it has been shown that the rate of habituation is related to the kind of stimulus used (Table 4). However, retention of habituation is relatively short and there is complete recovery of the withdrawal response in less than 24 hours in worms habituated to a series of sudden increases in illumination.

Fatigue can also result in the loss of a response to repeated stimulation and, in habituation experiments, it is obviously important to ensure that this is not occurring. However, it can be shown that ragworms, which have habituated to a series of, say, shadows are not suffering from muscular fatigue because they are still capable of responding to other kinds of stimuli, such as tactile ones. Similarly, fatigue of sense organs, which would result in insensitivity to stimulation, can be precluded as an explanation of the failure to respond in habituated ragworms because one response is sometimes replaced by an alternative one during the habituation process. For example, worms which no longer withdraw to repeated tactile stimulations at the anterior end are still sensitive to the stimulus because they often attack the seeker used to stimulate them and seize it with their jaws.

It seems curious that ragworms should habituate to stimuli that might warn them of the approach of a predator. But many of the stimuli that are caused by predators in Nature are also caused by harmless agents. Shadows, for example, are cast by passing clouds and seaweed floating in the water as well as a variety of crabs, birds and fishes, which prey on ragworms. Withdrawal is obviously important when a predator is approaching, but is unnecessary when the stimulus is innocuous and could even lead to an enormous loss of energy and feeding time. Habituation can therefore be seen as a mechanism that allows for a compromise between the conflicting needs of an animal which must feed at the end of its burrow and yet escape from predators. Any solitary stimulus is likely to herald the approach of a predator so that it is advantageous if the worm contracts and withdraws into its burrow. But a stimulus that is repeated over and over again is less likely to have a harmful concomitant and, by habituating to it, the worm is able to carry out its normal activities.

Feeding responses, such as those of the spiders *Araneus* and *Uloborus* to vibrations in their webs also habituate to repeated stimulation. These spiders respond to vibrations from struggling prey or from a vibrating tuning fork in contact with the web by orientating themselves towards the source of stimulation and running there. If the artificial stimulus is presented repeatedly, they learn to ignore it. First, the run to the source stops, although individuals still turn in that direction, then the turn disappears and preception of the stimulus is only indicated by movements of the legs, and finally even these movements cease.

The feeding behaviour of the waterboatman *Notonecta* also habitates to repeated stimulation. If a wire is dipped into the water near one of these animals it reacts by turning towards and swimming to the wire (see page 36). However, if the stimulus is repeated at four-second intervals the response gradually wanes and, as it does so, swimming to the source of stimulation stops and turns in that direction become incomplete.

It is not easy to relate habituation of feeding responses to the animal's needs because both spiders and waterboatmen depend upon vibratory stimuli for initial detection of their prey so that there is a danger that habituated individuals will no longer investigate potential prey. It is not surprising, therefore, that habituation of these responses is extremely slow. Waterboatmen usually respond to several hundred stimuli before habituating and spiders often run to the source of vibrations for more than a hundred trials. But even habituated animals are unlikely to starve, because any slight change in the nature of the stimulus re-elicits a response. For example, spiders which have habituated to a stimulus at one locus in the web respond again if vibrations occur at a different locus. Similarly waterboatmen, which have stopped responding to a wire dipped into the water on one side of the body, react to the same stimulus on the other side of the body as if they had no previous experience of it.

But feeding responses do not always habituate slowly. For example, exploratory responses of octopuses to inedible objects habituate rapidly to repeated stimulation. A blinded octopus usually explores an unfamiliar cylinder by holding it with its tentacles and taking it to the mouth. There is then a delay of several minutes before the cylinder is rejected. However, the octopus soon learns to reject a cylinder if it is presented to it on a number of occasions and does so in a matter of seconds, without even taking it to the mouth. But, like spiders and waterboatmen, habituated octopuses are not prevented from investigating other objects; they have well developed abilities to distinguish between different objects by touch and a second cylinder, differing in size or texture, usually re-elicits the exploratory behaviour.

Associative learning in the octopus

Associative learning is usually regarded to be a higher form of learning than habituation and is almost certainly less widespread in occurrence. Unfortunately it has been investigated in a relatively small number of invertebrates and only one, the octopus, has been studied in detail.

In the laboratory octopuses can live indefinitely in large, well-aerated aquaria and, if bricks are provided in one corner, they set up home among them. Healthy octopuses feed on small animals, such as crabs, and leave their homes to attack the prey. They approach it by gliding smoothly over the bottom, until they are about 20 cm away, when they stop and suddenly pounce on it. Unfamiliar objects introduced into the aquarium are usually attacked cautiously, but if the octopus is rewarded for attacking by giving it a piece of food it learns to attack unhesitatingly whenever that object appears. Conversely, if the octopus is punished by a slight electric shock, it learns always to avoid the object.

Octopuses normally have little difficulty in learning to distinguish between two situations and can be trained to attack in one but to retreat in the other. For example, they can be trained not to attack crabs shown together with a white square, by punishing attacks, while continuing to attack crabs shown on their own. At first they attack in both situations, but this is followed by a period when crabs, with or without the square, are approached warily. Finally they attack consistently to 'crab-alone' presentations but not to 'crab-with-square' presentations (Figure 26).

Octopuses have well developed visual learning systems and can be trained to discriminate between a variety of different shapes, such as horizontal and vertical rectangles, by appropriately rewarding attacks in one situation and punishing them in the other. They are also able to learn tactile discriminations and octopuses, blinded by cutting their optic nerves, can be trained to distinguish between cylinders which differ in texture or weight if these are brought into contact with the arms.

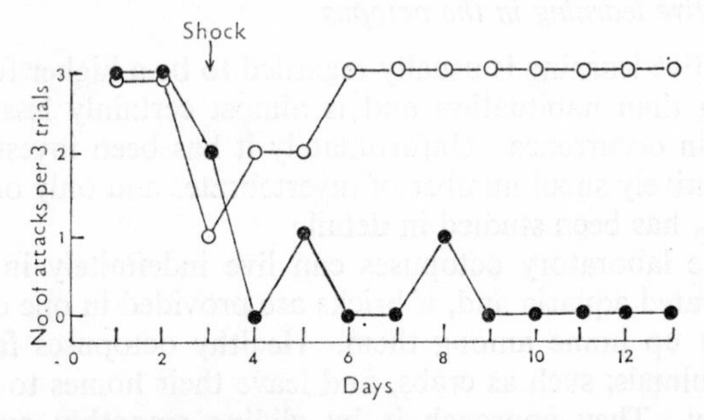

Figure 26. Results of a typical training experiment with *Octopus*. The animal was trained to discriminate between crabs presented on their own (—o—o—) and crabs presented with a white square (—•—•—). Three trials of each sort were given daily. For the first two days the octopus was allowed to eat the crabs in both situations, but thereafter it was punished with a slight electric shock for attacking in crab-plus-square trials. With training it soon learnt to leave these crabs alone while continuing to attack those shown on their own. (*After Boycott and Young*.)

It has been possible by suitable brain extirpation and lesion experiments to locate the nervous centres concerned in learning in the octopus. The brain, or more correctly, the supraoesophageal ganglion, consists of several distinct lobes (Figure 27) and parts of it can be removed without apparently upsetting the animal's innate behaviour so that the ability to learn can still be tested. Surprisingly, there are two largely independent learning systems: the visual learning system is found in the optic, superior frontal and vertical lobes, because the integrity of these lobes is necessary for successful learning by sight, and the tactile learning system is found in the inferior-frontal, subfrontal and vertical lobes. Apart from the vertical lobes, which are common to both systems, removal of part of one learning system does not seem to affect the other. For example, removal of the inferior frontal lobe, which is important in touch discriminations, does not affect the performance in a visual

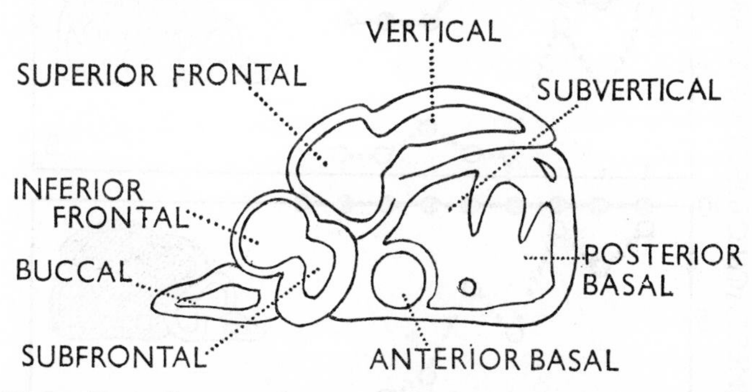

Figure 27. A diagrammatic section through the brain of an octopus showing some of the lobes concerned with learning (*see also Figure* 5; *page* 13). (*After Wells.*)

problem, such as learning not to attack a crab. On the other hand, removal of the visually important optic lobes, which constitute more than half the mass of the brain, does not prevent rapid learning of a tactile discrimination (Figure 28).

Vertical lobe removal has a similar effect on learning by touch and by sight so that it may have a common role in the two processes; learning in situations well within the capabilities of intact octopuses, is impaired if there is a long interval between the trials during training. For example, octopuses, lacking the vertical lobes, can still learn to discriminate in the 'crab alone' versus 'crab-with-square' experiment, but only if trials occur at short intervals of five minutes; when there is an interval of an hour between trials no learning occurs. Similarly octopuses without the vertical lobes can be

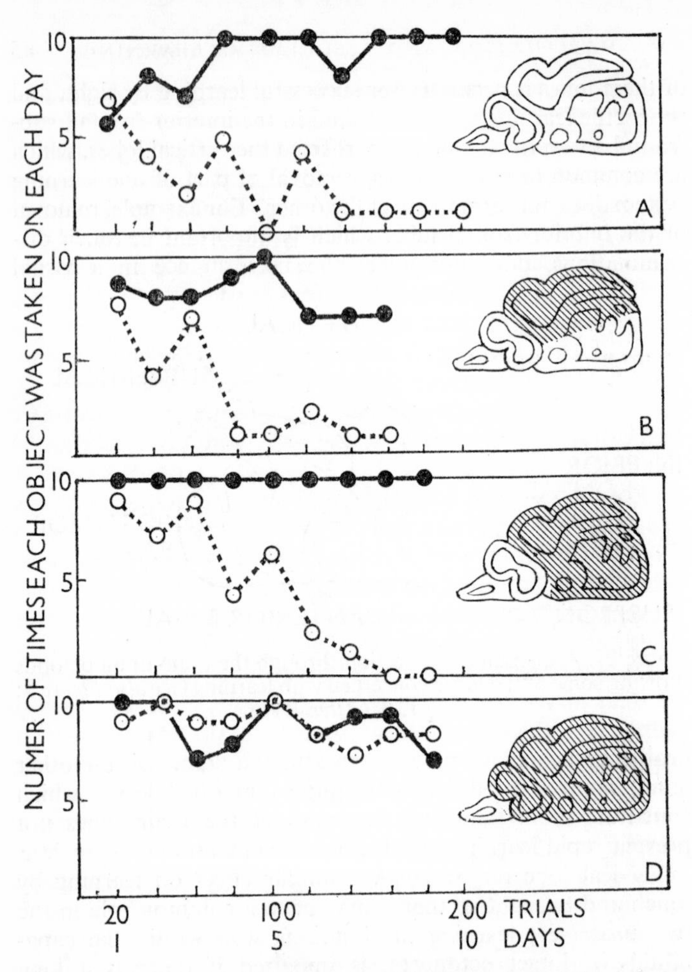

Figure 28. Results of experiments which illustrate that the inferior and sub-frontal lobes of the brain of an octopus are important centres for learning tactile discriminations. A: a blind octopus, which is appropriately rewarded or punished at each trial, is able to learn to take one cylinder to its mouth but to reject another one. B and C: after removal of large areas of the brain octopuses can still learn the discrimination. D: after removal of the subfrontal and inferior-frontal lobes, an octopus shows no evidence of learning. In C and D the optic lobes, which are not shown in the diagrams, were also removed. (*After Wells.*)

trained to discriminate between a smooth and a grooved cylinder if trials are given at the rate of forty per day, but they learn slowly or not at all if trials occur at hourly intervals. Clearly the vertical lobes play some part in the process of learning to recognise objects, but they cannot be the site of memory traces because an octopus can still be trained without them. In fact, it is becoming increasingly evident that the vertical lobes have several functions in the learning process, although some of them may be shared with other lobes (see below). One function is the transfer of a visually learned discrimination from one side of the brain to the other. By training an octopus in only one visual field and then testing it in the other it has been shown that there is almost total transfer of simple discriminations. For example, octopuses trained to distinguish between horizontal and vertical rectangles in one eye until they achieved a score of about 80% correct responses, scored a similar number of correct responses when tested in the other eye. Removal of the optic lobe on the trained side did not prevent transfer to the other side but there was no transfer when the vertical lobe was removed.

There is an interesting parallel between the effects of removal of areas of vertical lobe in *Octopus* and the cerebral cortex in mammals, which suggest that, in both, the organisation of learning depends upon the amount of nervous tissue present. The success of octopuses learning to distinguish between vertical and horizontal rectangles is related to the volume of vertical lobe tissue removed; errors increase as the amount of remaining vertical lobe tissue decreases (Figure 29). Similarly rats have more and more difficulty in solving problems in mazes as increasing amounts of cortical tissue are extirpated. The part of the cerebral cortex or vertical lobe removed is unimportant and, within wide limits, removal of the same amount of tissue from any part has the same effect on learning. Learning centres in mammals and cephalopods also have anatomical similarities; both the cerebral cortex in mammals and the visual and tactile centres in *Octopus* are characterised by the presence of numerous small cells. Thus, the visual learning centres in the octopus consist almost entirely of cells less than 5μ in diameter; the optic, vertical and superior frontal lobes contain, respectively, 95·6%, 99·7% and 97·4% of these cells.

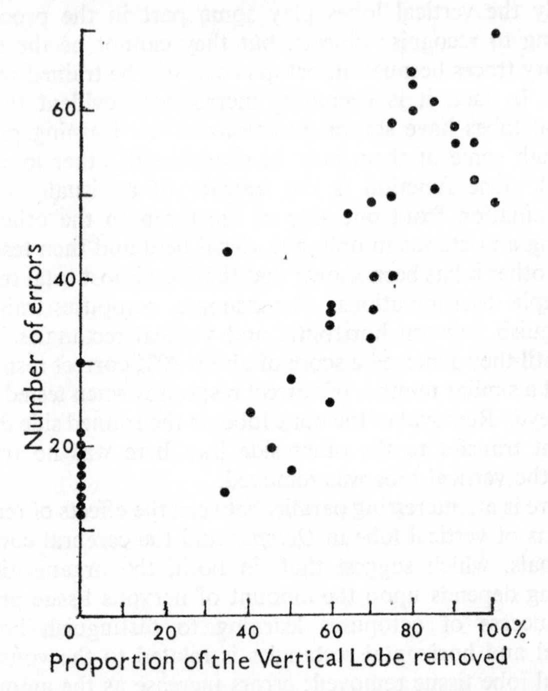

Figure 29. The relationship between learning to discriminate between horizontal and vertical rectangles and the proportion of vertical lobe tissue removed in octopuses. Errors increase as the amount of vertical lobe tissue removed increases. (*After Young.*)

Associative learning in insects

Among invertebrates, the learning capabilities of cephalopods are rivalled only by insects. Directly comparable discrimination techniques have not been explored, but there is no doubt that some insects are capable of learning in complex situations.

For example cockroaches, *Periplaneta orientalis*, and ants, *Formica incerta*, seem to have little difficulty in learning the shortest route through a complex maze (Figure 30).

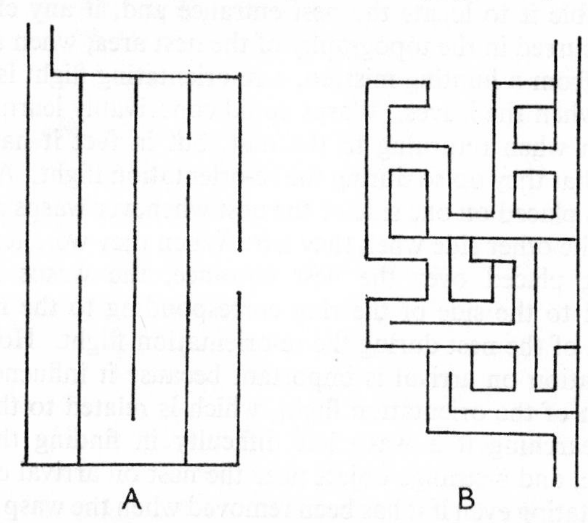

Figure 30. Mazes used in training experiments with (*a*) cockroaches and (*b*) ants. (*After Lawson.*)

Some of the most impressive evidence of learning in insects is provided by some of the solitary wasps of the family Sphegidae which have extraordinary abilities to learn the detailed topography of the territories around their nests. The female of one of these wasps *Ammophila campestris* digs a nest and brings paralysed caterpillars to it as food for her developing larvae (see Chapter 1). When she leaves the nest to hunt for caterpillars she flies from it, but the prey is too heavy to be brought back on the wing and is dragged along the ground. It is remarkable that she can find her way back to the nest by foot because the original learning of the territory is presumably made by observation from the air.

Another sphegid wasp, *Bembix rostrata*, captures flies and brings these back to the nest on the wing. Each time the female *Bembix* leaves the nest she carefully closes the entrance from the outside and it is extremely difficult for a human observer to locate it. But a wasp rarely has difficulty; in one investigation there were signs of searching for the nest entrance in only two out of 244 observed arrivals. *Bembix* learns visual clues that enable it to locate the nest entrance and, if any changes have occurred in the topography of the nest area, when a wasp returns from a hunting mission, a re-orientating flight is made over it when she leaves. Wasps could conceivably learn a new situation when returning to the nest, but in fact it has been shown that they do so during the re-orientation flight. A black ring was placed on one side of the nest whenever wasps arrived but on the other side when they left. When they were tested to the ring placed over the nest entrance, the wasps always returned to the side of the ring corresponding to the relative position of the nest during the re-orientation flight. However, the situation on arrival is important because it influences the duration of the orientation flight, which is related to the time spent searching if a wasp has difficulty in finding the nest entrance, and a strange object near the nest on arrival elicits a re-orientating even if it has been removed when the wasp leaves.

Unfortunately very little is known about the role of the nervous system in learning in arthropods, but it is difficult to imagine that 'higher centres' are not involved in complex maze and territorial learning. However, relatively simple responses can be learned in some insects without these centres. Cockroaches and locusts can learn to hold a leg above a saline solution if the leg receives electric shocks every time it dips into the saline. Decapitation does not affect the ability to learn, and both headless and intact insects learn the response in about 15 minutes. Learning can even occur in one ganglion of the ventral nerve cord because isolated preparations of the prolegs and first thoracic segment were also able to learn to hold a leg above the saline.

Learning in annelids and flatworms

Research on lower invertebrates has been less successful than that on cephalopods and arthropods and there is still disagreement about the levels of organisation at which animals can acquire learned associations. There are claims that conditioning is possible in all of the major animal phyla, including the Protozoa, but many are based on inadequate experimental evidence and some have been refuted by subsequent research.

Many of these experiments have used the classical conditioning procedure in which an unconditioned stimulus, which elicits a particular innate response, is presented at the same time as a neutral or conditioned stimulus. After a number of trials in which the two stimuli are presented together the animal learns to associate them and, as a result, both are capable of eliciting the response proper to the unconditioned stimulus. But, one of the difficulties in conditioning experiments on lower invertebrates, which may have led to the misinterpretation of some experimental results, is that the repeated effects of an unconditioned stimulus on its own can modify an animal's responses to the conditioned stimulus. This process, which is known as sensitisation, can occur when either a reward or punishment is used as the unconditioned stimulus and sometimes gives a false impression of conditioning. The presentation of food sensitises responses of the common ragworm *Nereis diversicolor* to sudden increases in illumination. In the laboratory individual worms, inhabiting glass tubes, can be fed on wheat germ extract placed near the exit of the tube; the worms crawl along their tubes, seize the food with their jaws and devour it. They usually respond to the light stimulus by withdrawing, although in one investigation 4 out of 19 worms (21·1%) responded by crawling to the ends of their tubes. However, a single presentation of food modified the behaviour of these worms to the light so that, when they were fed and then retested to the light 30 minutes afterwards, 12 of them (63·2%) responded in this manner.

In an experiment designed to investigate conditioning of the feeding response in ragworms, an experimental group was trained by presenting food (unconditioned stimulus) at the same time as the light intensity was suddenly increased (conditioned stimulus). These worms appeared to learn to associate the two stimuli because, when they were tested to the light only, they reacted more rapidly and more frequently by crawling along their tubes than a control group, which was subjected to the light but never fed. However, worms in a second control group fed between presentations of the light were as reactive as worms subjected to the paired stimuli. Clearly food presentation was sensitising the reactions of these control worms to the conditioned stimulus, because even mammals would find it difficult or impossible to learn the association under these circumstances, and presumably the food was having the same effect on the experimental group's responses to the light.

Sensitisation can also modify the behaviour of *Nereis* in more elaborate learning experiments, such as an avoidance learning problem, in which worms were punished for crawling along a Perspex channel by giving them a slight electric shock at the exit. Individuals of *Nereis virens*, *Nereis diversicolor* and *Perinereis cultrifera* were able to learn to avoid the punishment consistently, either by reversing and leaving the channel by the entrance or by remaining stationary in it, in an average of 21·5, 47·8 and 47·0 trials, respectively. But, surprisingly, even this modification in behaviour seems to be due to the repeated effects of the punishment. Worms could be trained as effectively by giving them shocks between trials, when they were not in the apparatus, as by punishing them at the exit of the channel (Figure 31). Similarly, punishments given to worms without any experience in the apparatus affected their behaviour as soon as they were introduced into it.

The difficulties of interpreting the results of experiments of this kind are underlined by the work on maze learning in annelids. A ragworm introduced into a simple T-maze (Figure 32) crawls rapidly to the junction and then either along the right- or left-hand arm. At first its selection of arms is random, but if it is punished for choosing one arm by giving it a mild electric shock and rewarded for choosing the other by allowing it to crawl into the dark compartment, its performance improves until, eventually, it avoids the punishment altogether by consistently choosing the correct arm. Three different

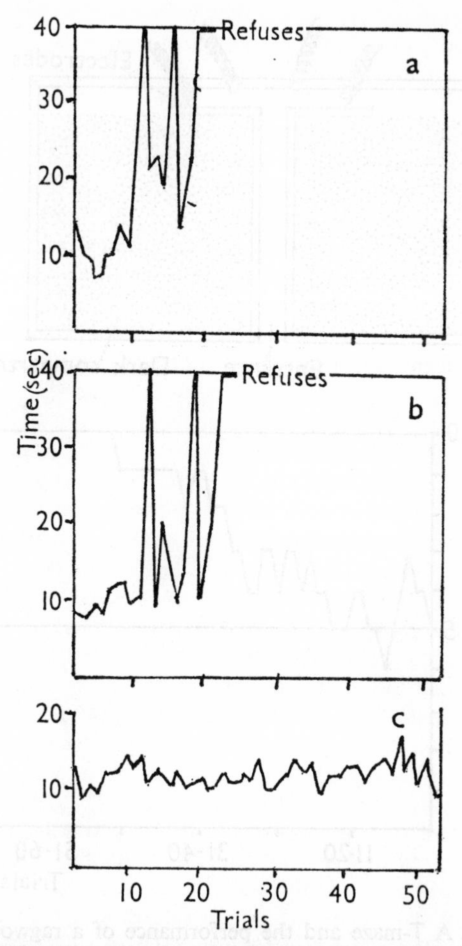

Figure 31. The time taken for individual ragworms to crawl to the end of a Perspex channel. (*a*) Punishment between trials (when the worm was not in the apparatus); (*b*) punishment at the exit of the channel; (*c*) no punishment. (*After Evans.*)

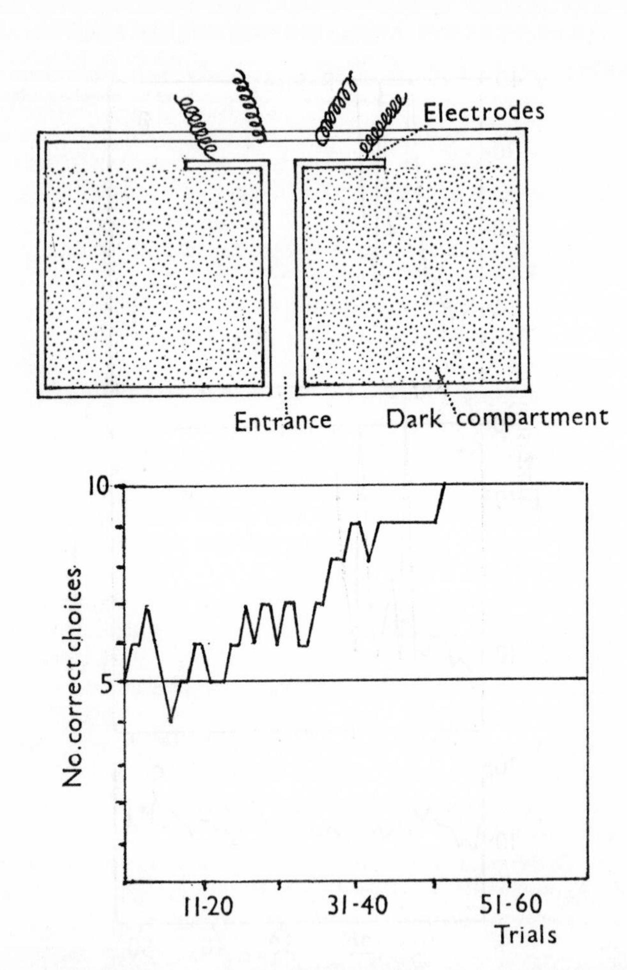

Figure 32. A T-maze and the performance of a ragworm, *Nereis virens,* in it. The worm was trained to turn consistently to one side at the junction of the maze by punishing it with a slight electric shock whenever it turned towards the other side. 'Correct choices' were rewarded by allowing the animal to crawl into the dark compartment and to remain there for five minutes. (*After Evans.*)

species tested in T-mazes could all be trained to a criterion of ten consecutive, correct choices in this way; *Nereis virens* in an average of 68·2 trials; *Nereis diversicolor* in 85·5 trials and *Perinereis cultrifera* in 85·0 trials. Earthworms can also acquire the habit of turning to one side in a T-maze and do so in about the same number of trials as ragworms.

These results provide the most convincing evidence of associative learning in annelids, but even this is not entirely unequivocal. It has been shown that earthworms subjected to either tactile stimulation or strong illumination on one side of the body turn towards the other side if they are subsequently tested in a T-maze. This cannot be used to explain the turning habit of worms trained in the usual maze learning procedure because the punishment for choosing the incorrect arm is not given unilaterally. Nevertheless, it does raise the interesting possibility that associative learning is not the only means by which an animal's behaviour may become modified so that it selects the correct arm in a T-maze.

However, the claims that animals at simpler levels of organisation than annelids are capable of conditioning cannot be ignored, even if it is eventually established that annelids themselves are incapable of learning in this manner. One group, the planarians, has received more attention than annelids and, although there are difficulties in interpreting results, there are several authors who claim to have demonstrated associative learning in these animals. In the first controlled conditioning experiments by Dr. J. McConnell and Dr. R. Thompson, 10 *Dugesia dorotocephala* were trained by pairing sudden increases in illumination with electric shocks. Responses were recorded to the light in each trial, before the shock was administered. At first, *Dugesia* responded infrequently to the light by either contracting or moving its anterior end from side to side. But with training responses increased from 28% in the first 50 trials to 43% in the last 50 trials, in an experiment lasting for 150 trials. The difficulty in interpreting these results is in deciding whether the increased reactivity was due to an association between the shock and light or to the sensitisation effects of the shock. A control group of 10 *Dugesia*, which was subjected to 150 shock only trials and tested to the light after every fifth trial, was certainly less reactive than the experimental group, but the worms did not receive the same total number of light presentations as the experimental worms so that it is not a valid control.

Results from experiments in which 30 *Phagocata gracilis* were trained in a discrimination problem are perhaps more convincing even if the situation was somewhat 'un-natural' for a planarian. When *Phagocata* receives an electric shock it turns towards the cathode so that, by appropriately arranging the electrodes, worms can be forced to turn either to the right or to the left. Their ability to learn to turn in a certain direction each time a stimulus was presented was tested by pairing forced turns to one side with a vibratory stimulus and forced turns to the other side with a sudden increase in illumination. Training lasted for 200 trials; in half of them the vibration and shock were presented together and in the other half light and shock were paired. Then, at intervals, the worms were tested to either the vibratory stimulus or the light presented alone. Apparently *Phagocata* can learn the association because, although turns to the correct side occurred in only 20% of the initial test trials, these had increased to 50% by the end of the experiment.

The nature of learning mechanisms

One of the exciting prospects of research into invertebrate learning is the possibility that, because of their relatively simple nervous systems and limited behavioural repertoires, it may be possible to understand the mechanisms involved in associative learning. So far the work on the octopus has made the greatest contribution in this field. Recently Professor J. Z. Young has postulated a memory system in the octopus that is based on the evidence of brain lesion and extirpation experiments, which were briefly discussed earlier in this chapter, and a detailed knowledge of the anatomy of the octopus brain. The nervous connections of the learning centres are well established by histological work and there are doubts about the existence of the circuits in Young's system in only a few instances (Figure 33).

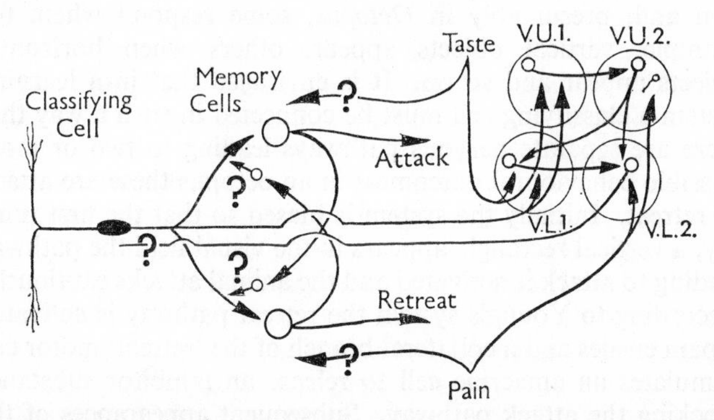

Figure 33. Young's hypothesis showing a single unit of memory in the visual learning system of the octopus. The classifying cell would only respond to a specific visual stimulus, say, the appearance of a vertical rectangle. It is connected so that either attack or retreat pathways can be activated. However, initially the system is biased so that the first time the cell is stimulated the octopus attacks cautiously. But, if pain ensues, the retreat pathway is activated by a collateral branch and a memory cell secretes an inhibitory substance blocking the attack pathway. On subsequent stimulation of the classifying cell the retreat pathway will then be activated. Alternatively, if reward ensues, a memory cell secretes inhibitors blocking the retreat pathway so that the animal will attack when the classifying cell is next stimulated. The long circuits between the four lobes in the diagram and the classifying cell probably 'keep the address' of the latter until the results of the animals action (pain or reward) have been received. The connections shown in the diagram are known to exist, except where there are question marks. V.U.1 = median superior frontal lobe; V.U.2 = vertical lobe; V.L.1 = lateral superior frontal lobe; V.L.2 = sub-vertical lobe. (*After Young.*)

Despite the independence of touch and visual learning centres there is no reason to suppose that learning is not organised in the same way in both systems and, certainly, there is a comparable arrangement of nervous connections.

The visual learning system is shown in Figure 33. The classifying cells in the optic lobes are specialised to record certain features of visual change in the environment. In mammals each classifying cell responds to a particular visual configuration and, presumably in *Octopus*, some respond when, for example, vertical objects appear, others when horizontal objects appear and so on. It is envisaged that in a learning system a classifying cell must be connected in such a way that there are separate nervous pathways leading to two or more possible behavioural outcomes; in an octopus these are attack or retreat. Initially the system is biased so that the first time, say, a vertical rectangle appears in the visual field the pathway leading to attack is activated and the animal attacks cautiously. According to Young's system the retreat pathway is activated if pain ensues and a collateral branch of the 'retreat' motor cell stimulates an amacrine cell to release an inhibitor substance blocking the attack pathway. Subsequent appearances of the rectangle will then activate the retreat pathway and the octopus will not attack but will avoid the rectangle. However, if attack is rewarded, the retreat pathway will then be blocked by the release of an inhibitor from the relevant amacrine cell and the octopus will 'learn' always to attack in that situation.

In any learning system there is a delay between the receipt of the stimulus by the distance receptor systems and the results of the action taken by the animal. For example, in training experiments the appearance of the vertical rectangle is followed sometime later by the reward or punishment. It is, therefore, necessary to keep the system active in some way and, thereby, 'hold the address' of the classifying cells stimulated until the results of the action are received by the learning centres. The circuits in the vertical and superior frontal lobes probably remain active in this way holding the address of the relevant classifying cell. But these lobes undoubtedly have other functions including generalisation of learning and transfer of learning from one side of the brain to the other (see page 87).

Young's hypothesis is concerned primarily with the physiological mechanisms of learning, but research on mammals and planarians has investigated the biochemical basis of memory. The protein ribonucleic acid (RNA) was first implicated in the learning process when it was shown that there was an increase of about 10% in the RNA content of learning centres in rats, which were taught to reach food with one paw rather than the other or to balance up a wire at an angle of 45°. Later the possibility that learning may involve a modification of RNA was tested by injecting RNA extracted from trained animals into animals which have received no training. Amazingly it seems that it may be possible to transfer learned behaviour in this manner. Untrained rats and hamsters, which received an injected extract of RNA from the brains of animals trained to respond to the sound of a click or a flashing light by going to a feeding box, turned towards the box significantly more often when tested to the experimental stimuli, than controls, which received an injected RNA extract from untrained animals. There have, however, been more recent reports from investigators who have been unable to replicate this result so that the question is still an open one.

Planarians have also been the subjects in transfer experiments, but because of the difficulty in interpreting the original training experiments (see page 95) it is difficult to assess the significance of these results. There is one claim that there was transfer of learning from a group of planarians trained in the light/shock conditioning technique when these worms were cut up and fed cannibalistically to untrained worms and another that the enzyme ribonuclease, which catalyses the breakdown of RNA, prevents normal retention of a learned habit if it is injected into a trained host. But it is not known what effects injected ribonuclease has on its host or whether the RNA ingested in the cannibalism experiments survives the digestive processes so that, even if planarians can learn associatively, many questions need to be answered before a direct link between RNA and the learning process is established in these animals.

But, despite these difficulties, there is no doubt that these experiments have stimulated a great deal of interest in the learning abilities of invertebrates. This in itself is valuable because, as the work on octopuses shows, invertebrates are likely to make an enormous contribution to our knowledge of the mechanisms underlying the behaviour of animals.

Reading List

General Reading

Baerends, G. P. (1959). Ethological studies of insect behaviour. *Ann. Rev. Entom.*, **4**, 207–233.

Bastock, M. (1967). *Courtship: A Zoological Study*. Heineman Educational Books.

Carthy, J. D. (1958). *An Introduction to the Behaviour of Invertebrates*. Allen and Unwin.

Carthy, J. D. (1965). *The Behaviour of Arthropods*. Oliver and Boyd.

Carthy, J. D. (1966). *The Study of Behaviour*. Arnold.

Thorpe, W. H. (1963). *Learning and Instinct in Animals*. Methuen.

Tinbergen, N. (1951). *The Study of Instinct*. Oxford.

Tinbergen, N. (1958). *Curious Naturalists*. Country Life Ltd.

Tinbergen, N. (1965). *Social Behaviour in Animals*. Methuen.

Papers and books referring to specific topics

Chapter 1. *Introduction*

Baerends, G. P. (1941). Fortpflanzungsverhalten und Orientierung der Grabwespe *Ammophila campestris*. *Jur. Tijd. voor. Entom.*, **84**, 71–275.

Brower, L. P., Brower, J. V. and Cranston, F. P. (1965). Courtship behaviour of the Queen butterfly *Danaus gilippus berenice* (Cramer). *Zoologica*, **50**, 1–40.

Crane, J. (1955). Imaginal behaviour of a Trinidad butterfly, *Heliconius erato hydara* Hewitson, with special reference to the social use of colour. *Zoologica*, **40**, 167–196.

Fankhauser, G. and Reik, L. E. (1935). Experiments on the case-building of the caddis fly larva *Neuronia postica* Walker. *Physiol. Zool.*, **8**, 337–358.

Harker, J. E. (1960). The effect of perturbations in the environmental cycle of the diurnal rhythm of activity of *Periplaneta. J. exp. Biol.*, **37**, 155.

Highnam, K. C. (1964). Hormones and behaviour in insects. *Viewpoints in Biology*, **3**, 219–256.

Manning, M. (1956). Some aspects of the foraging behaviour of bumble-bees. *Behaviour*, **9**, 164–201.

Tinbergen, N., Meeuse, B. J. D., Boerema, L. K. and Varossieau, W. W. (1942). Die balz des Samtfalters *Eumenis* (= *Satyrus*) *semele. Z. Tierpsychol.*, **5**, 182–226.

Vowles, D. M. (1961). Neural mechanisms in insect behaviour. In *Current Problems in Animal Behaviour* (edited by W. H. Thorpe and O. L. Zangwill). Cambridge Univ. Press.

Chapter 2. *Courtship Displays and Aggression*

Alexander, A. J. (1959). Courtship and mating in the buthid scorpions. *Proc. zool. Soc. Lond.*, **133**, 145–169.

Alexander, R. A. (1961). Aggressiveness, territoriality and sexual behaviour in field crickets (Orthoptera: Gryllidae). *Behaviour*, **17**, 130–223.

Clark, R. B. (1961). The origin and formation of the heteronereis. *Biol. Rev.*, **36**, 199–236.

Crane, J. (1949). Comparative biology of salticid spiders at Rancho Grande, Venezuela. Part IV. An analysis of display. *Zoologica*, **34**, 159–214.

Crane, J. (1957). Basic patterns of display in fiddler crabs. *Zoologica*, **42**, 69–82.

Manning, A. (1964). *Drosophila* and the evolution of behaviour. *Viewpoints in Biology*, **4**, 125–169.

Chapter 3. *Feeding*

Baerends, G. P. (1950). Specialisations in organs and movements with a releasing function. *Symp. Soc. Exp. Biol.*, **4**, 337–360.

Banks, C. J. (1957). The behaviour of individual coccinellid larvae on plants. *Anim. Behav.*, **5**, 12–24.

Pantin, C. F. A. (1950). Behaviour patterns in lower invertebrates. *Symp. Soc. Exp. Biol.*, **4**, 175–195.

Tinbergen, N. (1935). Über des Orientierung des Bienenwolfes. II. Die Bienenjagd. *Z. vergl. Physiol.*, **21**, 699–716.

Wells, G. P. (1950). Spontaneous activity cycles in polychaete worms. *Symp. Soc. Exp. Biol.*, **4**, 127–142.

Chapter 4. *Location of the Host by Parasites*

Beck, S. D. (1965). Resistance of plants to insects. *Ann. Rev. Entom.*, **10**, 205–232.

Dethier, V. G. (1957). The sensory physiology of blood sucking arthropods. *Exp. Parasitology*, **6**, 68–122.

Ilse, D. (1937). New observations on responses to colours in egg-laying butterflies. *Nature*, **140**, 544–545.

Lees, A. D. (1957). The sensory physiology of the sheep tick *lxodes ricinus*. *J. exp. Biol.*, **25**, 145–207.

Mann, K. M. (1962). *Leeches* (*Hirudinea*). Pergamon.

Thorpe, W. H. (1938). Further experiments on olfactory conditioning in a parasitic insect. The nature of the conditioning process. *Proc. Roy. Soc. B.*, **126**, 370–397.

Thorpe, W. H. and Jones, F. G. W. (1937). Olfactory conditioning in a parasitic insect and its relation to the problem of host selection. *Proc. Roy. Soc. B.*, **124**, 56–81.

Chapter 5. *Movements*

Den Boer, P. J. (1961). The ecological significance of activity patterns in the woodlouse *Porcellio scaber* Latr. (Isopoda). *Arch. Neerland. Zool.*, **14**, 283–409.

Edney, E. B. (1954). Woodlice and the land habit. *Biol. Rev.*, **29**, 185–219.

Fraenkel, G. and Gunn, D. L. (1964). *The Orientation of Animals*. New York: Dover Publications.

Lees, A. B. (1961). Clonal polymorphism in aphids. *Symp. Roy. Ent. Soc. Lond.*, **1**, 68–79.

Newell, G. (1958a). The behaviour of *Littorina littorea* under natural conditions and its relation to position on the shore. *J. mar. biol. Ass. U.K.*, **37**, 229–239.

Newell, G. (1958b). An experimental analysis of the behaviour of *Littorina littorea* under natural conditions and in the laboratory. *J. mar. biol. Ass. U.K.*, **37**, 241–266.

Passi, F. (1955). Experiments on the sense of time in *Talitrus saltator* (Montagu). *Experientia*, **11**, 201–202.

Southwood, T. R. E. (1962). Migration of terrestrial arthropods in relation to habitat. *Biol. Rev.*, **37**, 171–214.

Waloff, N. (1941). The mechanisms of humidity reactions of terrestrial arthropods. *J. exp. Biol.*, **18**, 115–135.

Williams, C. B. (1958). *Insect Migration.* Collins: New Naturalist Series.

Chapter 6. *Escape Responses*

Blest, A. D. (1957). The function of eye-spot patterns in the Lepidoptera. *Behaviour*, **11**, 209–256.

Bullock, T. H. (1953). Predator recognition and escape response of some intertidal gastropods in the presence of starfish. *Behaviour*, **5**, 130–140.

Crane, J. (1952). A comparative study of innate defensive behaviour in Trinidad mantids (Orthoptera; Mantoidea). *Zoologica*, **37**, 259–293.

De Ruiter, L. (1952). Some experiments on the camouflage of stick caterpillars. *Behaviour*, **4**, 222–232.

Roberts, M. B. V. (1962). The rapid response of *Myxicola infundibulum* (Grübe). *J. mar. biol. Ass. U.K.*, **42**, 527–539.

Yentsch, C. S. and Pierce, D. C. (1955). Swimming anemone from Puget Sound. *Science*, **122**, 1231–1233.

Young, J. Z. (1938). The functioning of the giant nerve fibres of the squid. *J. Exp. Biol.*, **15**, 170–185.

Chapter 7. *Social Behaviour*

Butler, C. G. (1957). Some work at Rothamsted on the social behaviour of honeybees. *Proc. Roy. Soc. B.*, **147**, 275–288.

Butler, C. G. (1962). *The World of the Honeybee.* Collins: New Naturalist Series.

Free, J. B. (1956). A study of the stimuli which release the food begging and offering responses of worker honeybees. *Anim. Behav.*, **4**, 94–101.

Lindauer, M. (1961). *Communication Among the Social Bees.* Harvard Univ. Press.

Lüscher, M. (1961). Social control of polymorphism in termites. *Symp. Roy. Ent. Soc. Lond.*, **1**, 57–67.

Wallis, D. (1961). Food sharing behaviour of the ants *Formica sanguinea* and *Formica fusca*. *Behaviour*, **17**, 17–47.

Wilson, E. O. (1963). The social biology of ants. *Ann. Rev. Entom.*, **8**, 345–368.

Chapter 8. *Habituation and Associative Learning*

Clark, R. B. (1960a). Habituation of the polychaete *Nereis* to sudden stimuli. 1. General properties of the habituation process. *Anim. Behav.*, **8**, 82–91.

Clark, R. B. (1960b). Habituation of the polychaete *Nereis* to sudden stimuli. 2. Biological significance of habituation. *Anim. Behav.*, **8**, 92–103.

Evans, S. M. (1966). Non-associative behavioural modifications in nereid polychaetes. *Nature*, **211**, 945–948.

Griffard, C. D. and Peirce, J. T. (1964). Conditioned discrimination in the planarian. *Science*, **144**, 1472–1473.

Horridge, G. A. (1964). The electro-physiological approach to learning in isolatable ganglia. *Anim. Behav. Suppl.*, **1**, 163–182.

Van Iersel, J. J. and van den Assem (1964). Aspects of orientation in the digger wasp *Bembix rostrata*. *Anim. Behav. Suppl.*, **1**, 145–162.

Rose, S. (1965). Is learning transferable? *New Scientist*, **28**, 781–782.

Szlep, R. (1964). Changes in the response of spiders to repeated web vibrations. *Behaviour*, **23**, 203–239.

Thompson, R. and McConnell, J. V. (1955). Classical conditioning in the planarian, *Dugesia dorotocephala*. *J. comp. physiol. Psychol.*, **48**, 65–68.

Wells, M. J. (1962). *Brain and Behaviour in Cephalopods.* Heinemann Educational Books.

Wolda, H. (1961). Response decrement in the prey catching activity of *Notonecta glauca* L. (Hemiptera). *Arch. Neerl. Zool.*, **14**, 61–89.

Young, J. Z. (1964). *A Model of the Brain.* Clarendon Press.

Young, J. Z. (1965). A unit of memory. *New Scientist*, **28**, 861–863.

Index